Augment It

Grammar Factory Publishing
MacMillan Company Limited
25 Telegram Mews, 39th Floor, Suite 3906
Toronto, Ontario, Canada
M5V 3Z1

www.grammarfactory.com

Nourbakhsh, Mehdi
Augment It: How Architecture, Engineering and Construction Leaders Leverage Data and Artificial Intelligence to Build a Sustainable Future / Mehdi Nourbakhsh PhD

Paperback ISBN 978-1-98973-752-1
Hardcover ISBN 978-1-98973-754-5
eBook ISBN 978-1-98973-753-8

1. TEC004000 TECHNOLOGY & ENGINEERING / Automation. 2. ARC015000 ARCHITECTURE / Professional Practice. 3. TEC009000 TECHNOLOGY & ENGINEERING / Engineering (General).

Production Credits
Cover design by Designerbility
Interior layout design by Dania Zafar
Illustrations by Pierre Langlois
Book production and editorial services by Grammar Factory Publishing

Grammar Factory's Carbon Neutral Publishing Commitment
From January 1st, 2020 onwards, Grammar Factory Publishing is proud to be neutralizing the carbon footprint of all printed copies of its authors' books printed by or ordered directly through Grammar Factory or its affiliated companies through the purchase of Gold Standard-Certified International Offsets.

Disclaimer
The material in this publication is of the nature of general comment only and does not represent professional advice. It is not intended to provide specific guidance for particular circumstances, and it should not be relied on as the basis for any decision to take action or not take action on any matter which it covers. Readers should obtain professional advice where appropriate, before making any such decision. To the maximum extent permitted by law, the author and publisher disclaim all responsibility and liability to any person, arising directly or indirectly from any person taking or not taking action based on the information in this publication.

Augment It

How architecture, engineering and construction leaders leverage
data and artificial intelligence to build a sustainable future

MEHDI NOURBAKHSH, PHD

To Samaneh, my classmate, my colleague, my co-founder, my love, my wife, and my better half.

Testimonials

My biggest AI challenge is calibrating my roadmap. Adoption of AI into business sits between hype and reality: are we doing enough, are we progressing fast enough? Or are we being dragged into an expensive distraction by talented influencers? Building a proportionate roadmap is the biggest challenge of every leader and every individual when confronted with a new technology with so much promise. I am concerned about this and need answers, but after reading this book I have greater confidence in being able to create an agile roadmap to de-risk our future progress. *Augment It* is "straight from the horse's mouth," and allows you to get your knowledge straight from the applied research teams in leading AEC firms. If we are going to discuss AI in AEC, read this book before we talk. This is going to save a lot of time for everyone in AEC who wants to mobilize technology. If you want to look ahead, stand on the shoulder of your peers to see further.

Alain Waha, CTO of Buro Happold

Like many in AEC, we struggle with the erosion of profit margins, or 'write-downs,' due to uncertainty and lack of predictability in our industry. The erosion of our profitability is an ongoing frustration, because other industries also face risks associated with lack of certainty but have been able to mitigate those risks in ways that few do in AEC. When AI is appropriately applied, it can help AEC firms mitigate risks and unpredictability by leveraging historic project data for reliable predictive analytics. Mehdi explains a potentially daunting topic in an approachable way. Pick this book up and learn a thing or two about what AI can do specifically for our AEC industry!

Dace Campbell, Director of Product Management in Construction at McKinstry

AI is quickly gaining traction, and even more quickly gaining hype in the industry. It is difficult to keep track of the emerging methods, how they might apply to different aspects of our business and, frankly, where to start. Mehdi's book is an engaging and informative guide to the different kinds of AI, how to think about the value of each to your specific business, and how to start and scale successful AI projects. The book is a surprisingly entertaining read with helpful mnemonics and memorable anecdotes that help you retain and reapply the content. If you are looking to better understand how AI can impact the industry and your firm, this is the book for you.

John Haymaker, Director of Research at Perkins & Will

Construction has always been a single-item production, and as the business expands, the more complex the performance requirements become and the more manpower is needed. But AI has the potential to overturn that idea. Also, until now, most of the knowledge and experience accumulated by architects/engineers was lost with the death of the individual, but now we can think of it as being renewable at any time. In other words, AI can come alongside you as a digital architect/ engineer. *Augment It* contains concrete cases and covers a wide range of applications from upstream to downstream in the construction industry, making it easy to apply to your own situation. This book will provide a comprehensive view of the changes that AI is bringing about in the construction industry, an industry that has been around for a long time but is not familiar to the general public. In addition to the use of AI, the construction industry is experiencing a variety of digital transformations. However, it always starts with planning. AI will be used to plan a wide range of tasks.

Yoshito Tsuji, General Manager of the Design Department at Obayashi Corporation

Right out of the gate, this book addresses the basics of AI and its relevance to common problems faced by the construction industry. I recommend this book to AEC executives who want to learn more about AI and how it is likely to impact our industry in the near future.

James Detzel, Director of Innovation at Austin Commercial

This is the first book to explain how AI can be applied to construction-industry problems without all the marketing hype from the technical world.

Eric Law, Co-founder & CEO of Urban Machine and former
Senior Director of Innovation at Swinerton

Get your free workbook

To help you run your first AI project successfully, I have provided an accompanying workbook that contains workshop activities, as well as AI planning and execution documents, on our website. This is all you need to run your project like a champion!

You can download it for FREE at www.augmentit-book.com or by scanning the QR code below.

Contents

ABOUT THE AUTHOR

Mehdi Nourbakhsh, PhD, finds novel solutions for demanding problems.

Mehdi is an author, speaker, and the CEO of YegaTech, a technology consulting company in the AEC industry. He's devoted to helping CEOs, CTOs, innovation directors, and business executives grow their business and differentiate themselves and their companies via AI technology and innovation.

With more than a decade of experience in research and development of innovative AI solutions at YegaTech, Autodesk and the Georgia Institute of Technology, Mehdi brings a unique perspective to the architecture, engineering, and construction (AEC) industry. He has been involved in leading and advising on several AI solutions that are used by tens of thousands of AEC and manufacturing professionals every day. He has also filed more than six US patents on the use of artificial intelligence in the AEC and manufacturing industries, given various thought leadership talks at Autodesk University, run workshops, taught AI courses at various venues and universities, mentored start-ups, and served as a member of the technical advisory committee of the Center of Integrated Facility Engineering at Stanford University.

Mehdi graduated from the Georgia Institute of Technology with a PhD in building construction and a master's degree in computer science. He has worked as a structural engineer and construction manager on various large commercial and industrial projects.

He believes people should move their energy away from doing tedious and mundane tasks, and towards creative and productive tasks in order to make a better built environment. That's why he started his consulting company, YegaTech — to help AEC professionals and companies grow by curating their data and creating AI technologies with a significant return on investment.

Mehdi lives with his wife, Samaneh, and dog, Goofy, in San Francisco, California. He is an avid runner, and loves to swim in pools or lakes (as long as he can see the bottom).

mehdinourbakhsh.com

PREFACE

I wrote this book because I believe that if we all put our heads and hands together, we can change the architecture, engineering, and construction (AEC) industry for the good of people and the planet. In short, I wrote this book because I believe in the power of "we." Together, we can change how we design and build to improve our industry and create a sustainable, diverse, inclusive, and equitable planet for all of us to live on.

As an industry, we need to innovate and increase the pace of change, technology creation, and adoption. If I could say just one thing to our industry, it would be: "You can change faster; you can do it." There are a million reasons not to change or to say that this is impossible, but it only takes one company and one person in that company to lead the way, and then the rest will follow.

And that person could be you, my beloved reader. Yes, you! I wrote this book for you because I believe that, using the steps in this book, you can invent, innovate, and augment your capabilities to create a better world. I hope you will join me in pushing this industry forward. Together, we can.

Mehdi Nourbakhsh, PhD

INTRODUCTION

Tom was the new CTO of a design and construction company in London. Part of his job was to identify opportunities for process improvements and technology implementation. He heard from various executives of the company that the board was becoming interested in how emerging technologies, especially AI, could be used in their day-to-day operations. But for Tom, AI seemed to be far away, despite all the hype in the news. (Perhaps it feels the same for you, too?) He could not see clearly how AI could be relevant to the day-to-day workflow of designers and builders within the company. Nevertheless, as a technology thought leader in the organization, he knew that sooner or later some other executives or colleagues would either ask his opinion about it or, even worse, the CEO or the board would ask him to investigate how it may impact the business in the long term.

Tom had many questions: What is AI? What are the use cases of AI in our business? How does investing in AI give us market differentiation? He kept asking these questions in his head before finally opening up his laptop to do a Google search for the answers. He thought to himself, "I'm going to spend a couple of hours online and get to know the ins and outs of AI. Then I'll be good to answer any questions that the CEO or the board might have."

His simple search "What is AI?" returned almost four trillion results in 0.65 seconds! Tom went through the first three pages, only to realize that there was a big problem: he found three different and conflicting definitions of AI, a couple of which did not even make sense. The information was either too technical or too shallow, as if it was written for computer scientists or people outside of the AEC industry.

The more Tom read, the more questions were created in his mind and the more puzzled he became. It was a fearful moment for him, because he had expected that a quick Google search could help him to find answers to his questions. But his search only left him confused and intimidated. It took almost three weeks of research for Tom to realize that AI and machine learning are not the same thing, even though people use the terms interchangeably.

How does this resonate with you?

How many times have you searched for some clear information about machine learning and AI, only to feel even more lost and confused as you sift through conflicting explanations that you are not even sure are true? This is a big waste of time — time that you could be spending on better design and construction for our built environment.

The internet is full of conflicting definitions and articles about AI written by and for scientists and people outside of the AEC industry. Therefore, it is extremely difficult for AEC professionals to know what AI really is or is not.

This is not only Tom's story. As an AEC professional, I've been there too, and I've done that. That's how I know.

I will never forget my first days of learning about AI. At the time, I wasn't just doing a Google search: I was at university completing my master's in computer science, and had all the support of a formal educational environment. But because I was in the master's program, all of our textbooks were at the advanced level. So, since I didn't have a bachelor's degree in computer science, I had to study all the basics that were taught in the undergraduate program on my own. And I was struggling, because the internet was full of nonsense and conflicting messages about AI and its techniques. At least I had a professor to go to for help to determine the difference between what was fact and what was fiction, but lots of AEC professionals (like you) don't have the time to talk to them. That's why I am driven to make AI more accessible and understandable to you and our industry.

The challenges in AEC, and how AI can help

A lot has changed in the architecture, engineering, and construction industry in the past two decades. The complexity of projects in design and construction has increased. Clients are asking for more in design, and they want the construction projects to be on budget and on time while satisfying sustainability and environmental requirements. All of this needs to be done despite the shortage in skilled labor and the retirement of many knowledgeable professionals.

With all these challenges in front of us, the next several years and decades will be extremely difficult. You not only need to be profitable, but also environmentally sustainable and conscious while dealing with a lack of productivity and resources, as well as a broken supply chain. You need to gain power and influence over many internal and external variables and issues at the same time. You need to take control, exert mastery, and stay on top of your market competition.

The good news is that a lot has changed in technologies outside and inside the industry over the last two decades. Outside of the industry, the cost of making scalable technology has gone down significantly. We now have access to high computing power at a substantially lower price (and it's only getting cheaper!). In addition, algorithms and software have been becoming both more powerful and more accessible to people.

Inside the industry, we are becoming more tech-savvy despite the slow adoption of technologies such as building information modeling (BIM), project management information systems, mobile platforms, drones, virtual and augmented reality, smart sensors and RFIDs, 3D printing, robotics, and artificial intelligence. But these technologies are not being adopted equally.

In KPMG's Global Construction Survey for 2019 [1], 223 senior leaders and executives from design and construction companies around the globe were divided into three groups: innovative leaders (top 20%), followers (middle 60%), and behind the curve (bottom 20%). The survey showed that even among the innovative leaders, while the investment and implementation of BIM and project management information systems are among the highest in the industry (86% and 83%, n=155), investment in artificial intelligence is one of the lowest (24%), making it one of the most underutilized technologies in AEC. Despite where these leading companies are today, the executives of the innovative companies believe that:

"Intelligent equipment, machine learning and artificial intelligence (AI) will become commonplace in the next five to ten years."

According to PWC's report "Sizing the prize: What's the real value of AI for your business and how can you capitalize?" [2], AI is estimated to contribute $15.7 trillion to the global economy by 2030. The report states that:

> *"In the near-term, the biggest potential economic uplift from AI is likely to come from improved productivity. This includes automation of routine tasks, augmenting employees' capabilities and freeing them up to focus on more stimulating and higher value-adding work."* [2]

Similarly, in "Notes from the AI Frontier: Modeling the impact of AI on the world economy" [3], McKinsey's Global Institute explains:

"Those that establish themselves as AI leaders could capture an additional 20–25% in economic benefits compared with today... There could also be a widening gap between companies, with front-runners potentially doubling their returns by 2030 and companies that delay adoption falling behind... the extent to which companies choose to use AI for innovation rather than efficiency gains alone are likely to have a large impact on economic outcomes."

With the decrease in the cost of technology and significant improvements in computing and algorithms, digitization of AEC, and availability of data, lots of leading AEC companies are investing or going to invest in AI technology and developing their own AI solutions.

We are at the tipping point - leading AEC companies that harvest their data and develop their own AI solutions to differentiate themselves in the market will win more projects and create positive impact, while others will wait to a point that is too late to take advantage of this underutilized technology.

Some people ask why we should build our own solutions – why not wait for others to build off-the-shelf solutions for us? Sure, these are all potential options on the table. However, keep in mind the risks and challenges coming from these choices. Vanilla technologies built by others are usually generic solutions, and are not tailored to your specific needs and conditions. Moreover, those technologies are available for everybody, including your competitors, so it doesn't give you any competitive advantage.

To win against your competition and increase your market differentiation, you need to utilize your data and build your own AI solution, because nobody knows your problems better than you and you are likely to have all the data you need to solve the problem right now (and if you don't, there are ways of obtaining it). This solution is tailored for the requirements, conditions, and resources you have.

After working in the AEC industry as a structural designer and construction manager, and working with AEC executives to develop AI technologies as a solution provider, here is my recommendation for you:

Utilize your data and build your own AI solution, because nobody knows your problems better than you and you probably have all the data you need to solve the problem right now.

You may not know exactly how to use your data and leverage AI to solve the problem, but this will change after reading this book.

What this book is – and isn't

I wrote this book for CEOs, CIOs, CTOs, innovation directors, and AEC executives and leaders who are not satisfied with the status quo and want to fast-track success and bullet-proof their business against the uncertainties of the future. This is also a book for implementers, managers, and strategists who want to lead their team and organization in the age of AI, and for anyone interested in the AEC industry who wants to learn how they could be impacted by AI.

However, this book is *not* written for an AI engineer or scientist who wants to know about the details of AI algorithms or the math behind it. It provides a general overview of the field of AI and does not go into the theories behind any specific AI sub-fields, such as machine learning, computer vision, and optimization, as there are many other books about those subjects. Nor is this book for people who want to work *in* their AI projects as a developer or technician; rather, it's for those who want to work *on* their AI project as a manager and leader.

What to expect

As part of my research for this book, I interviewed and worked with more than fifty AEC professionals from companies like Mortenson, Swinerton, Austin Commercial, Suffolk, ConXtech, McCarthy, Haskell, Gensler, Perkins & Will, CannonDesign, Woods Bagot, Buro Happold, Obayashi, GHD, Strategic Building Innovation (SBI), MWH Constructors, VIATechnik, VHB, Nike, BAGs, and HD Labs. I asked these professionals two key questions: 1) How can I make this book more beneficial to our industry? and, 2) what should I include in the book that has the most value for my readers? With the feedback I received, I created, refined, and fine-tuned the material that I'm now excited to share with you in this book.

When interviewing AEC executives, it was interesting to see that business executives from both design and construction companies are looking at using AI as part of a sustainable future, but that they had their own respective, nuanced definitions of the term "sustainable future." The sustainable future for design companies was about increasing the quality of design and improving the building occupants' experience while saving our environment and the planet. For construction companies, a sustainable future entailed not only this, but business metrics as well – especially those related to return on investment.

Whatever one's definition of a sustainable future is, I believe that design and construction should come together. That's why I did not split this book in two for design and construction professionals. I have various examples and use cases of AI for architects, engineers, and construction managers throughout the book. These examples include use of data and AI in the conceptual design of buildings, prefabricated structural steel and building assemblies, job-site inspection, quality control, and business growth.

This book has everything you need to learn about, experiment with, and scale AI in your company. Part 1, "Why AI is Your Secret Weapon," lays out the challenges putting pressure on AEC professionals, discusses the opportunities that AI is creating in response to these challenges, and explains why investment in AI is essential.

In Part 2, "AI Education," you will learn exactly what AI is and is not, how data can add value to your company, and the five characteristics of data that you should consider in running your AI and data projects. You will learn about AI systems and their limitations and biases, and you will also learn how Perkins & Will, McCarthy, and Swinerton use AI systems in design, prefabrication, and construction.

At the end of Part 3, "AI in Action," you'll know how to find AI use cases in your company. Once you have identified the right AI opportunity, you'll learn about the process of developing your AI solution. After you've done your first AI project, it'll be time to put everything together and define an AI strategy for your company. As you work your way through Part 3, you'll find activities that you can do with your team. To help with these activities, you can use the accompanying workbook, available at www.augmentit-book.com.

Finally, Part 4, "AI in Practice," presents three contemporary case studies of real companies experimenting with AI in the areas of conceptual design, business growth and sales, and construction inspection.

My story

At this point, you may be wondering about my own journey working in the AEC industry, and how I ended up as a consultant developing AI technologies for AEC companies like yours. Right after completing my undergraduate program in civil and structural engineering in 2007

I started my professional career as a structural engineer, working in a design and construction company. After several months of designing high-rise commercial buildings, I moved to construction sites as a project manager to build the structures that I designed.

What a gift to move from the design to the construction department! As a designer, I never cared much about how my design would be built. That's someone else's problem, I used to say. However, when I started building my own designs, my whole perspective on structural engineering changed. In addition to focusing on stability and serviceability, working on the site opened my eyes to how to design for constructability.

Back when I was working on construction sites we had lots of problems, including managing change, lack of productivity, and shortage of labor. I remember a day when half of my workers didn't show up because it was the harvesting season, and they could make more money in a safer environment! Then there were the days when we had to train farmers to work on construction in the evening.

I fell in love with working with people on site, and decided to get a formal education in construction. After taking a master's in construction management, I started my PhD in building construction and design computing at the Georgia Institute of Technology, where I designed, taught, and developed various AI algorithms for design and construction. To strengthen my AI- and technology-building background, I completed a master's in computer science while I was doing my PhD program.

The reason I became interested in learning about AI was the challenges that I faced from the lack of skilled labor in construction. I had a vision that with AI, we could preserve the knowledge of our skilled laborers and make their expertise accessible across various projects and on different sites. I called my vision "the augmented worker." And it's a vision that I still have.

My journey in AI did not stop with my PhD program. Before

completing my degree requirements, I was invited to join Autodesk as an AI research scientist. What I liked about my job there was working with so many bright people, and spending many hours with AEC professionals in design and construction companies to shadow their work and learn about tough problems where AI can contribute a significant business value. We brainstormed ideas, prioritized AI use cases, and developed AI solutions with at least a tenfold return on investment that have also had a positive impact on the planet.

I want you to have the same or an even more positive impact on the planet and your bottom line. That's why I wrote this book – and why I know AI can help.

My three wishes for you

When writing this book, I thought a lot about three secret wishes I had for my readers, which I'd like to share with you now.

First, I wish that this book helps you identify AI use cases, develop tailored AI technologies, and define AI strategies that bring tremendous value to your company. I wish that whatever use cases you decide on bring significant market differentiation and a sustainable future for your company.

Second, I wish you can take the learning from this book to do something amazing in the world and have a positive social and environmental impact beyond the immediate benefits for your company. It could be designing a refugee camp in less time, retrofitting homes and infrastructures in emerging nations to be hurricane-proof and earthquake-resistant, or building shelters for low-income people or those who need them the most. I wish you will do something great for the good of other people and the planet.

Third, I wish you to share the learnings from your AI projects so you can help advance your industry as a whole, and also continue your

AI journey after reading this book. This last wish is why I created work-shops and training courses for AEC professionals who are interested in staying up to date with what's latest in AI technology in AEC, and bring those innovations into their projects and companies. You can find more information about the upcoming industry share-outs, workshops, and training materials at www.mehdinourbakhsh.com. Come to the workshops and our regular gatherings to meet likeminded people, who might be at the same level as you or ahead of you in their AI journey.

One last note before we take off. AI is an emerging field, and things that are new today will be old by tomorrow. So, I did my best to stock this book with foundational information that won't get old. If you would like to stay up to date with current AI trends, please feel free to join my AI newsletter at my website.

Are you ready to start building your future?

Let's go.

PART 1

Why AI is your secret weapon

The AEC industry is the industry of superheroes. In a typical super-hero movie, evil external forces invade a city, a country – or even the whole universe – without warning. The authorities cannot find an effective, systematic way to defeat them using their everyday arsenal of weapons. So, they turn to superheroes who have the extraordinary powers and knowledge needed to defeat the invading forces. Every mission is unique and different, requiring heroes with specific skills, powers, and strategies.

Just like the mission that is central to most superhero movies, every AEC project takes place in a unique location, with specific requirements and goals. So, AEC companies assemble and deploy their highly skilled "heroes" to complete their design and construction mission.

But unlike a superhero movie, in which the heroes rarely age or lose their powers, the superheroes of the AEC industry are beginning to retire. That personnel attrition, plus the growing global climate emergency, increased project complexities, lower profit margins, and lack of productivity, brings lots of pressure to our industry. This is why we need to think differently and solve our problems systematically.

Technology (and more specifically AI) is one of the weapons the AEC industry can draw on to help solve these problems. AI technology, if built the right way, can partner with us to reduce project complexities, advise us based on the patterns of past projects, and codify the valuable, hard-earned knowledge of our AEC superheroes for generations to come, ensuring that it will never be lost.

In Part 1 of this book, we will review some of these industry challenges and discuss the opportunities of using technology and AI to decrease pressure and increase productivity and profitability. Then, you will learn about why and how you should invest in AI technology. In addition, you will learn about some of the most commonly held AI myths that could potentially stop you from learning and experimenting with the technology. At the end of Part 1, you'll be ready to kick off your AI journey!

CHAPTER 1

The challenges and opportunities

I will never forget the first day of my work as a structural engineer at
Chapar, a design and construction company specializing in commercial
and industrial buildings. I was so excited and had so much ambition to
change the way structural engineers design buildings. We used to use
CSI's SAP and ETABS to design building structures, and I was able to
connect those into various scripts that I wrote to automate the design
process. But a few months into the job, I got bored with designing. The
challenges were different from one building to another, but the fundamental principles and method were the same. After all, I automated
most of the process, so there was nothing to do other than modify CAD
files and produce detailed drawings.

Thinking about what I wanted to do next, I observed and worked
with some of the architects in the company, thinking that I might join
their department if I found myself interested in what they do. Their
biggest problem back then was having to do too much modeling and
CAD work, and not enough work on ideating and creating new concepts. This was the opposite of what I wanted to do, so it was a big no
for me! Instead, I talked to our CEO and suggested that I could be a
more valuable asset to the company if I learned how to build buildings.
He thoughtfully accepted my proposal, and my construction management journey began.

Working as a construction manager was very different from working in the office as a structural engineer. I loved the teamwork, collaboration, and leadership aspect of being a construction manager. However, we had lots of challenges in managing and completing projects on time and on budget, especially due to the lack of skilled labor.

Our industry has changed a lot over the last two decades, but many of our problems have stayed the same, or even gotten worse. Even though we had a shortage of labor back then, it's nowhere close to the shortage we have today. In addition to suffering from the retirement of senior skilled labor, the construction industry of today has become unattractive to the younger generation because of the lower pay, slower pace of technology adoption, poor health and safety records, and lack of gender diversity compared to other industries [4][5]. Also, back then we didn't care too much about building performance or sustainability in design and construction, although we should have. Needless to say, a couple of decades ago, the projects were less complex than what we design and build today.

Besides these problems, we have lots of new problems that were not an issue back then. In a workshop with about twenty global industry thought leaders, I captured some of the challenges they have in their design and construction practices today:

- Design for building performance is time-consuming, given the short project execution time.
- Design for manufacturing and fabrication is new for our designers; we need a paradigm shift.
- Our design teams are not trained to consider esthetics, environment, and fabrication/construction all at the same time.
- Clients want us to deliver the project faster, with no delays.
- We should put extra time and effort into reporting the embodied carbon of all major activities on sites.
- Reduced schedule, being on a budget, doing safe and quality work, while reducing the embodied carbon? Are you kidding me?

- We are training farmers to work part-time in our construction projects.
- The cost of skilled labor in our region is skyrocketing.

How many of these challenges can you relate to?

I've heard different flavors of these statements in various engagements and in every workshop I run: industry fragmentation, broken supply chain, extensive regulations, misalignment of intensives, and many other problems that you're already well aware of. I also heard about these challenges from the industry thought leaders that I interviewed in preparation for writing this book. So, I decided to summarize these industry challenges into three categories: pressure from clients to do more, lack of productivity in design and construction, and low profitability. Let me briefly explain each of these challenges by sharing how the industry experts see these problems.

The architecture, engineering, and construction industry is now dealing with three main challenges: Pressure, Productivity, and Profitability.

Challenge 1: Pressure

In the commercial and industrial sectors, clients are demanding more. In the past, clients asked to reduce the cost and time of projects. Today, however, the awareness of climate change and the desire from clients to act on it has increased. In other words, in addition to insisting that designers and contractors meet time and cost restraints, clients are rightly demanding buildings that perform efficiently and meet energy, embodied carbon, and other sustainability requirements.

How have you felt pressure in delivering the design or construction of your projects?

Pressure on designers

Architects need to manage several conflicting goals and constraints placed upon them by their clients: the design has to meet the client's budget while still functioning well, and it must be completed in a very short timeframe.

There is more overlap between the design and construction activities in new AEC contracts (e.g., design-build) compared to traditional contracts such as design-bid-build. Just a couple of years ago I went to a billion-dollar construction project in San Francisco, where I learned that the design team was developing construction drawings at the same time that construction on the project was beginning. There were just a few weeks between the time that the design was developed and the time that the construction of that design began. Because of the iterative nature of the design practice and the limited time they had before construction, the design team was feeling a lot of pressure.

The head of design of a US-based company told me that:

"We feel a lot of pressure to design high-performing buildings under a given project budget. Given the typically short time we have for some high-end commercial projects, we make lots of trials-and-errors, which bring a tremendous amount of waste into the process. In other words, we redesign for budget and performance several times, and unfortunately, in some projects, buildings are not working as they are supposed to."

Architects are under pressure to do more (manage several of their clients' conflicting goals and constraints) in less time.

Pressure on contractors

Similar to the situation with designers, contractors are becoming responsible for satisfying more client requirements. They need to find ways to reduce not only time and cost, but also the carbon footprint from their operations. In my conversation with Eric Law, director of innovation at Swinerton, a commercial construction company in the United States founded in 1888, he shared that:

"For many years, our clients have been asking us to build more cost-effectively in a shorter time. Now they're starting to add in sustainability. Therefore, as a company, we have to minimize and report to our clients three major metrics: time, cost, and embodied carbon. So every time our clients make changes, we must tell them the impact of their change on these metrics. For instance, if they change the material of the structure, or the supplier or subcontractor, we should calculate and report the change in embodied carbon of the project. These new metrics and demands put lots of pressure on contractors."

Contractors are under pressure not only to reduce cost and time, but also to reduce and report embodied carbon every time clients make changes.

Challenge 2: Productivity

It is no surprise that productivity in construction is significantly lower than in other industries. According to McKinsey, "[the industry's] annual productivity growth over the past twenty years was only a third of total economy averages" [6]. Consequently, this low productivity costs the global economy $1.6 trillion a year [7]. Among all the root causes of low productivity – such as increased project and site complexity, extensive regulation, the fragmentation of the industry, bespoke owner requirements, poor project management and execution, and lack of skilled labor – the main issue is "lack of thoughtfulness and investment in upfront planning and design," according to McKinsey's partner Mukund Sridhar [7].

Construction is facing major productivity problems because of a lack of thoughtfulness and investment in upfront planning and design.

Productivity in design

On the design side, architects and engineers spend a lot of time working with clients who may not know exactly what they want. Often, as architects are making progress in their design, clients will change their minds and ask for something completely different. Redesigning projects based on evolving client requirements is very common and extremely counterproductive, because these changes then need to be coordinated with other design teams such as structural or mechanical engineering teams and external consultants.

Another challenge with design is that designers (rightfully) want to protect themselves against potential liabilities, so they design in 3D and then spend time to create and deliver 2D drawings (or, for some projects, low-fidelity models with legal disclaimers!). In addition, the architectural or engineering design often does not meet the construction requirements because of a lack of knowledge, incentives, or (again) the need to reduce liabilities. So it is very common that the design gets evaluated based on the construction resources and constraints in the value-engineering process. In almost every case, redesigning the design is inevitable.

There is a tremendous amount of inefficiency in the whole design process today.

Productivity in construction

On the construction site, contractors need to build bespoke designs in a bespoke way! The buildings may have a unique design, and they may be being built in a specific location by various subcontractors and groups of people who have never worked together before. These factors, along with the shortage of skilled labor and supervisors, bring a lot of productivity challenges to the industry. James Detzel, director of innovation at Austin Commercial, one of the most diversified builders in the United States, describes this issue:

> *"Conventional wisdom says construction will never match the productivity increases that are seen in manufacturing, since every construction project poses its [own] unique challenges and has many variables that change from one project to the next. Construction doesn't have the same opportunities to iterate and improve through mass repetition. With that said, there are components of the construction-project life cycle that can be repetitive. If these repetitive components can be identified and rigor applied to how*

*they are implemented, a large quantity of useful data can be gen-
erated that will create opportunities to iterate and improve."*

That's why, in recent years, the AEC industry has been moving
towards virtual prototyping to avoid potential conflicts before construction starts, and industrialized construction, to make entire buildings, or
part of buildings, as products. Now more than ever, design optimized
for fabrication and manufacturing has become extremely important.

Challenge 3: Profitability

I remember hearing a financial investor say, "With more risk, you get
more reward," and thinking to myself: that is the opposite of the AEC
industry, in which we take a lot of risk with almost no reward. After all
these years, AEC companies are still chosen to work on projects based
on the lowest bid or cheapest proposal, rather than their merits and
qualifications. The average bid-to-hit ratio for AEC companies is around
ten to one, meaning that out of ten projects they bid on, they may only
win one. Imagine if we could save the time and effort that goes into
bidding on projects – we could save billions of dollars!

Profitability in design

On the design side, 50% to 80% of the design fee is the cost of labor in
producing drawings. In a recent discussion I had with architect Tsuji
Yoshito, the general manager of Obayashi, Japan's leading design and
construction company, he explained that:

> *"The design fee is usually 7–10% of the cost of an entire project. For
> instance, if the entire budget of the project is $100 million, the cost
> of design is $10 million. Out of these $10 million, we spend about
> $5–6 million in labor fees to create 2D and 3D models and produce*

drawings. In terms of the number of staff required to complete a job, we have over twenty supporting staff for each star architect. This is a very time-consuming, inefficient, and expensive process."

Profitability in construction

Everyone who works in construction knows that it is a brutal business. Unexpected problems, interest rates in financing projects, fluctuations in the cost of materials and supplies, and delays in projects are some of the factors that impact the profitability of projects [8]. Having only a 4% to 5% profit margin for general contractors (and only slightly higher for some subcontractors) for taking a huge amount of risk puts the companies in a difficult position. That's why many companies over the past several years have tried to expand their presence and gain more ownership of the AEC value chain. Derek Cunz, executive vice president at Mortenson, a top-twenty US-based builder, developer, and engineering services provider, explains the profitability problem really well:

"Being a low-margin business creates significant challenges for the AEC industry. When most projects are won based on low fees and/or low bids, it is difficult to invest in innovation, grow business, or make significant changes. Investment in innovation and change requires a long view and efficient execution of projects to create value."

High risk and low profit margins are putting the AEC industry in a tight position for investment and growth.

What can AI do for you?

I wish I could say that AI is a magic wand that can solve all your problems. The reality is that it is not. Like any other technology, AI has its pros, cons, and limitations, which we'll discuss later in the book. The point is that, like any tool, you need to know what AI is, where to use it, and how to use it. With that in mind, I'd like to share some of my observations about opportunities where AI can help to overcome the "3P" challenges (pressure, productivity, profitability) we've been discussing.

Opportunity 1: Reduce complexity to decrease pressure

At the early stage of design or preconstruction, AI can help you design and plan your project based on various conflicting objectives and constraints. For example, AI can help designers analyze and optimize the design based on client budget and time while satisfying energy, daylighting, and sustainability requirements. While designers can also do this without AI, it takes longer (and can also be prone to human error). In a discussion that I had with Hilda Espinal, CTO of CannonDesign, she said:

> "We are working in an increasingly demanding environment where clients expect more while schedules and profits tend to shrink. The good news is that AI can significantly help overcome these challenges. How exactly? By merging the 'best of both worlds': where we identify when to use computing power and when to leverage our human abilities, to then apply them in tandem. Where AI is best suited for cases requiring the processing of large amounts of data, generation, and validation of design solutions or identification of trends and patterns, and our humanity is ideal for the more subjective aspects of design, such as empathetic interpretation and creativity."

AI can help designers reduce pressure by analyzing and optimizing designs based on various conflicting project goals and constraints in a short time.

Similarly, AI can reduce the construction complexity. If you are designing for manufacturing and assembly (DFMA), AI can help you bring all the fabrication and assembly requirements into the early design stage. Later, in Chapter 6, you will learn how teams at McCarthy are working on developing an AI recommendation engine that helps designers decide on prefabrication product options at the conceptual design phase. On the construction site, you can design your site with the help of AI or optimize your operation based on material, labor, or your supply chain. Eric Law, director of innovation at Swinerton, explains:

> "The labor challenge, materials escalation, and supply chain complexity are creating a whole new host of issues that the industry hasn't seen before. In the past, you've had a labor challenge or a material challenge, but they haven't all hit at once. Now we see our supply chain fall apart, and we are dealing with the material challenge while the labor costs go up. That's a very big risk and financial hit on some of our projects. If you don't understand those challenges deeply and are not prepared to optimize your operation, you'll face significant consequences. And this is where AI can play a big role. We've seen this with manufacturing and aerospace and how those industries leveraged AI to become more efficient. The cost of AI technology has come down significantly, and its capabilities have increased exponentially. This is the perfect time to start."

AI can help contractors reduce pressure by optimizing the site and operation for materials, labor, and supply chain.

Opportunity 2: Improve performance to increase productivity

Designers can use AI to get quick feedback about the performance of their buildings. For instance, AI can help with rapid cost estimation by running structural, acoustic, thermal, and energy simulations. This means you don't have to wait for a long time for the analysis software to run, or to hear back from the estimator or the engineer to tell you whether the building is within the budget or structurally stable, or what type of material is most suitable. In Chapter 6, you will learn how Perkins & Will is using AI to design high-performing buildings by reducing the time it takes to run an energy simulation from twenty to thirty minutes to less than a second.

AI can help designers to improve their design by providing quick feedback about their design performance.

As a contractor, AI can help you run your projects based on data and information rather than intuition. In a discussion with Niels W. Falk, CEO and head of consulting and innovation at HD Lab, a Denmark-based technology company, he shared with me his experience working in construction and how he sees the opportunity of using AI:

> *"In my experience, working on construction sites was like driving a car with a windshield that was painted black, and you could barely see through it. However, the car had a very big rearview mirror, and you could see everything that was done around you.*

In the back seat of the car, your companies' executives are drinking
champagne and screaming, 'Faster, faster,' but you have no idea
what you should do and what's in front of you. I think AI can help
us straighten some of this out so we can run projects on actual
data and information rather than on memories and experience."

In Chapter 4, you will learn how AI, by using predictive and
prescriptive analysis, can help you make data-driven and informed
decisions in the execution of your projects.

AI can improve the performance of contractors by helping them make
decisions based on actual data and information rather than intuition.

Opportunity 3: Reduce cost to increase profitability

Since 80% to 90% of the cost of your projects is materials and labor, a
minor improvement in these areas can potentially bring a lot of profit
to your company. AI can help you optimize the use of materials based
on your project requirements and the availability of your resources.
For instance, you can use AI to optimize the amount of concrete you
need in your project based on the type of formwork you have, the
availability of suppliers and materials around the project, or even the
embodied carbon.

On the design side, AI can help you with the creation and production of building geometry so that you can quickly communicate your
design with your client. With this, you'll have more time to work on
the creative part of your job rather than focusing on producing drawings
and 3D models just to show to your client. Teams at Obayashi developed
an AI solution that creates geometry based on design principles and data
from past projects. With this tool, their designers could significantly
reduce the number of design iterations and the time it takes to produce

them by co-creating the design with their clients. (This project is the first case study in Part 4.)

AI can help designers reduce costs by creating and producing building geometry and drawings quickly.

On the construction side, AI can reduce costs by automating tedious and repetitive tasks such as inspections. For instance, on a large construction site, tracking and monitoring the work-in-place can be challenging, time-consuming, and error-prone. Instead of sending a few people to the site, you can use an AI system to do the inspection and quantity take-off for you. This is what the team at Swinerton did: they used a robotic platform to inspect the site, create as-built and take-off quantities, and update their schedule (more about this in Chapter 6). Scaling this AI solution to hundreds of projects can save a significant amount of time and costs for your company.

Another example of cost-saving is welding inspection. It is very expensive to hire certified welding inspectors and send them to various construction sites across different regions. To reduce costs, superintendents often walk the site for random inspections and report the welding that is clearly wrong. AI can help improve this process and reduce the cost of operation by analyzing photos sent by welders when they complete each weld. This is the project that teams at Haskell have been working on. (You'll learn more about this in the third case study in Part 4.)

AI can help contractors reduce costs by automating tedious and arduous tasks such as inspection.

So, let's summarize everything we have discussed so far in this chapter.

Projects are becoming more complex, and clients are demanding more. Our productivity across the AEC industry is low because of the lack of skilled labor and the bespoke nature of complex projects. Compared to the risks taken, companies have a low profit margin because of bidding wars and the high cost of design and construction labor and materials.

With the growth in population and changes in climate, we need to do more – a lot more. And we need to do it with very limited resources, and in a very short period of time.

AI is not a silver bullet to solve all the problems ahead of us. But it is an underutilized technology that can help you to reduce the complexity of projects by running various scenarios and helping you make better decisions. It can help you improve the performance of your project either by giving you quick feedback about your design (e.g., the amount of embodied carbon) or helping you run your projects based on information. And, finally, it can help you to reduce costs. All of these things can happen while still fulfilling your obligations to your client and your company, and they will also have a positive environmental impact.

Before concluding this chapter, let's go back to the superhero analogy. Even though every project has unique aspects (e.g., site location), our materials, our teams, and our processes in design and construction are very similar from one project to another. One may argue that the job of our industry's superheroes is to find the balance between unique problems and standard best practices. Therefore, one opportunity of using AI could lie in finding the patterns in your problems and your solutions and making a match between them (like a recommendation engine). This way you can employ an agile workforce with high turnover and rely less on your legacy team. Such AI technology can change your products and services, your business model, and even your core competency in the market.

You will learn more about all this in Part 4, "AI in Practice." In the next chapter, however, you will learn about why and how you should invest in AI.

THE AEC CHALLENGE

Alain Waha is the CTO of Buro Happold, an international, integrated consultancy of design engineers and consultants known for delivering creative, value-led building and city solutions such as the Museum of the Future, the Jewel Changi Airport, and Detroit Future City.

I met Alain at one of the industry events in Boston, and had several discussions with him about the role of technology in business model transformation in AEC. He is a thought leader and a digital agitator who always thinks outside the box.

Alain has thirty years of industry experience: half in AEC, and half in tech R&D and automotive. He is passionate about mobilizing technology to solve real-world problems, often through business-model change. He has co-founded several start-ups since 1989, when he graduated with a master's of fluid mechanics from the University of Manchester.

His point of view about the challenges of the AEC industry is best explained in his own words:

I see the challenges of our industry in three time horizons. The first time horizon is what is happening now. We lack productivity and skilled labor, and there is low profit margin in designing and constructing complex buildings and infrastructures. These days, we often talk about the environment and net-negative or net-zero facilities. Still, the regulations are loose; they're optional or highly recommended, but not enforced widely. So, if clients ask for it, we'll do it; otherwise, we don't.

This situation is relatively easy compared to what will come in horizon two, when we have more internal and external pressure. The emergence of climate change with increased competition in the market, increased complexity, and significant productivity and labor shortage issues put us and the industry in a very tight spot.

In addition to all these challenges, we need to deal with complex environmental policies, regulations, and mandates about designing, procuring, building, and operating buildings. Building net-zero for the same price is becoming a norm in this competitive market.

The last horizon is when push comes to shove! Most of the construction will happen in emerging countries, because the construction in developed countries will have lots of restrictions or come to a halt. For instance, in major cities you can only reuse the existing buildings and cannot get permits to build new ones, or getting permits is becoming extremely difficult. Or, only net-zero or net-negative buildings may get approval. These buildings also have to be reconfigurable to address our more dynamic life and businesses, and to meet the circularity constraints. AEC companies are evaluated based on how much their design, construction, and operation meet environmental requirements such as reducing, reusing, and recycling.

We'll have more flash floods, earthquakes, hurricanes, and wildfires in the future. It means that we should build an entire city in a very short period while meeting complex and demanding requirements. This is a challenging problem that we'll deal with.

The only way we can take control of the highly challenging future is by using data and technology. Those who will thrive recognize that they are no longer a design or construction company – instead, they are a data and sustainability company, so they plan to manage their data and leverage AI to increase productivity and reduce complexity while having a positive impact. Our future depends on how open-minded we are to absorbing change and utilizing technology.

CHAPTER 2:

How (and why) you should invest in AI

I was working with Sara, the newly appointed CEO of a prefab company that designed, fabricated, and assembled building structures. I was appointed to find inefficiencies in their design process and develop an AI solution for their core technology.

In my scheduled one-on-one with Sara, she explained some of her biggest challenges. I listened carefully, taking notes as she detailed each one. After she finished, I looked at her and asked, "As a new CEO, why do you want to invest in AI technology?"

She smiled, slowly opened the drawer on the right side of her desk, and took out an old Nokia cell phone. She held the Nokia phone in her right hand and a new iPhone in her left hand and said, "Do you know why Nokia failed? One of the reasons was that they focused too much on their hardware technology and ignored the software side."

She then put the Nokia down and held the iPhone up. "I want my prefab solution to be like an iPhone: a solution that is a combination of hardware and software. I know that our building product is good; I want to make it the best in the market by creating an intelligent AI engine to design, customize, and optimize it based on project requirements and constraints."

A few months later, Sara had what she wanted. I created an AI solution that took in their kit-of-parts, procurement, fabrication and schedule constraints, and client budget and requirements to design an optimum structure in a few hours instead of weeks. They could manage change, design in less time, and save millions of dollars on projects.

The best part of the project process was the feedback that I received from Sara:

"Running our first AI project helped us understand what AI really is and what it can do for our products, our services, and our business. Besides learning about AI, the experience we gained from this project helped us to see our data in a different way. Now we know how to capture and organize our data and get the most value out of it. This would not have been possible without us investing our money and time in completing our first AI project."

Where is your company today, and where do you want it to be five years from now? How can AI help you to remove some of your business bottlenecks?

Besides all the learnings that come out of your first AI project, the technology, if chosen carefully, can help you improve and grow your business. In Part 4 you will learn how ConXtech, a leading design and construction company, uses AI to remove some of its business bottlenecks and improve its sales and business development activities. This growth does not come if you take no action or wait and see what happens – it comes when you have the right investment strategy.

What is your data and AI investment strategy?

You might be asking yourself, "I'm working in the AEC industry, not in the tech industry; why should I have a data and AI investment strategy?" Before answering this question, I want to clarify that when I say you should invest in your data and AI, I don't mean you should plan and build the next flying robot or autonomous bulldozer. Let the tech companies do that for you. What I mean is that you should have a strategy to find use cases and opportunities to use AI in areas where you want to gain or hold your competitive advantage in the market – for instance, if you have a secret sauce in estimating projects, designing buildings, or managing projects, and want to scale it across your company at your portfolio level. In Chapter 6, you will learn how teams at McCarthy use AI to harvest their lessons learned from individual projects and apply them to their entire project portfolio.

Historically, AEC companies have not invested in data and AI, but this is changing. More and more companies are investing in their digital transformation and AI to reap the benefit of this technology.

Based on my experience, we have a spectrum for AI technology investment in the AEC industry. On one end of this spectrum are some AEC companies that take a wait-and-see approach when it comes to technology, especially AI. Companies on the other end of the spectrum want to know how this technology can enable them to be different from their competitors, so they plan, find a budget, and try to experiment with and learn about it. There are also other strategies between these two ends of the spectrum. For instance, you might wait and see what technology makers bring to the market to solve some of your problems, but while you wait you might experiment and build your own technology for your core capabilities, or in the areas that give you market differentiation.

For the sake of simplicity, let's review the strategies on the two ends of the AI technology investment spectrum.

Wait-and-see

You believe that you are an AEC company, not a technology company. So, you wait for other companies to develop an off-the-shelf solution for you. You believe that you should be a technology *user*, not a *builder*, even for your own needs. When you share your problem with tech providers, you hear that they are working on it and will probably develop a solution soon, so why should you invest in that? After all, you may not have enough budget to invest in technology.

Pros:

- This strategy does not require a capital budget.
- There is less risk in not being first to market and having to learn hard lessons.

Cons:

- When technology providers bring their solutions to the market, all your competitors can use them as well – therefore, you don't gain a competitive market advantage by being the consumer of the technology.
- The off-the-shelf solution developed is one-size-fits-all; it has a lot more capability than you want, and it may not completely satisfy your unique needs and requirements.
- The ownership of data over a long period of time is not clear. Will these companies still exist? What happens if you no longer want to retain your data to avoid exposure in the case of litigation?

Do-it-yourself

You realize that in order to prepare yourself for future projects in such a competitive market, you need to tie technology and processes very closely together. Following tech companies and waiting for them to make technology available to everyone does not give you the competitive edge you need. So, you have started educating yourself about AI and plan to run a few experiments and projects, or you have already started your first project and are learning from it. This is what I highly recommend doing, especially for your core products or services.

Pros:
- Your solution is customized and tailored for you and your business.
- You have full control over what to build.
- You have full control over your data.
- You will get a competitive advantage that no other company has.
- If planned correctly, your solution will give you a very high return on investment (ROI) in the long term.

Cons:
- It may require initial capital to invest.
- You need to hire the right talent or technology partner.
- Your solution (if it's not built correctly) may not work as you expected.

What is your AI investment strategy? Wait-and-see, or do-it-yourself?

Wait-and-see is definitely the cheapest strategy, but with all the challenges in the market today and the uncertain road ahead of us, this could be a strategy for failure in the long run.

Do-it-yourself is the strategy that you should undertake. If you put time, energy, and money into chasing and trying various off-the-shelf options and into investing in yourself and building your own AI solution, I promise that you'll be unstoppable in the market. Connecting your products and services to an intelligent technology solution makes your company like a smartphone that gets better and better over time.

To be clear, I'm not saying you should stop using off-the-shelf products from vanilla technology providers, or that you should become a software company. The point is, you must invest in yourself to experiment and learn about AI – at least for your core products and services, where you can get market differentiation.

You need to have a strategy for finding the right opportunity that gives you the competitive advantage for winning and differentiating yourself from the market. That's why you should invest in AI.

Busting the mental AI myths

Before we move on, let me say that this is the point where I usually get a lot of objections. Some of the first things I often hear are, "How can we invest in AI when we don't even know where to store our data?" or "We need to crawl (organize data), then walk (run analytics), and then run (AI projects); we are crawling now." And my answer to executives who ask these questions is that this is not a sequential process.

To help illustrate this, let me share a story with you.

One of the companies that I've been working with decided to digitize and organize all its data. Their strategy was to use one of the cloud providers in the market so that everyone in the company could put all the information in using the same solution. After a year, they could run data analytics and they were very happy with it. I told them several times that they should run an AI project as soon as possible, but they wanted to collect data first. Two years passed, then they kicked off their first AI project.

In two years, they had been able to collect many CAD files, photos, issues, and RFIs. But there was one big problem: they could not export their data from the cloud provider the way they needed to for their AI project. All the links and connections between building models, RFIs, photos, issues, and other data they had were lost. "We could export terabytes of disconnected datasets, but they were useless for our AI project. If our executives had known what they should look for and what questions to ask, they would not have chosen this provider in the first place," said Ben, their chief data scientist, adding, "We are also missing lots of data that we have not been collecting."

The crawl–walk–run progression does not apply to data and AI projects. Let me explain.

The closest analogy I can think of is grocery shopping. Have you ever invited guests over for dinner, and gone grocery shopping *before* you decide what you want to make? Perhaps you bought lots of items, but the moment you decided what you wanted to make, you realized that you hadn't bought several things you needed for the recipe, or you bought steaks instead of ground beef! To apply this to our subject, your grocery items are like data, and your AI project is like a recipe. You don't want to collect too many grocery items (data) because, first, they are expensive, and second, they may go stale over time. Instead, you should think about what you want to create as the end goal or finished product, and use the "recipe" for collecting and organizing the right data.

You may think that you need to organize your data *before* thinking about or selecting an AI project. But the reality is that knowing what you want to do with data gives you an idea about what the gaps in your data are, and/or how you should capture and organize your data.

---

*Knowing the AI project you want to work on
gives you a recipe for collecting, organizing, and
managing data across your organization.*

Another objection I often hear from company executives is that running AI projects seems to be a long endeavor, and if they invest, they want to see the results in a quarter. I agree that some AI projects may need longer for data cleaning and preparation, but lots of AI techniques (such as optimization) don't need data, and can be implemented and used in a relatively short period of time – say three months, depending on the complexity of the problem.

For instance, if you want to optimize the cost of a concrete structure based on your construction process, availability of formworks, and suppliers around the project, you don't need data from hundreds of past projects (which you probably don't have anyway). Instead, you can define or model it as an optimization problem and run an AI solver to come up with solutions.

---

*Many AI projects can be done in a short time
and with a limited budget.
Lots of AI techniques don't need data. So, you don't necessarily
need to have data to run an AI project.*

Finally, lots of executives hear about AI projects and think that they're expensive and require a lot of upfront cash, which means they'll never get the buy-in from their company leaders. Now, keep in mind that there are two sides to this investment coin: capital investment and time investment. And sure, AI, like any other great tool, does need an initial investment on the capital front. But here's another way of looking at it.

Many years ago, carpenters extensively used manual tools like hammers and nails. Today, they have an advanced tool called a nail gun. Even though it is expensive to buy compared to a hammer, it has a huge return on investment (ROI) because of the increased productivity and quality of work. Therefore, the high ROI justifies the investment. Like the nail gun, artificial intelligence is a tool – a very powerful tool. A tool that can help you reduce work pressure, become more productive, and increase your profit over time with significant ROI.

There are two main differences between AI and a nail gun (aside from the obvious ones). Unlike the nail gun, you cannot buy AI solutions off the shelf, especially in the areas where you are uniquely different in the market: you need to build them on your own for your specific needs. Another difference is that you don't have to invest a huge amount of money up front to develop your AI solution: you can create, find, and prioritize the best AI use case for your company and execute it over time (more on this in Chapter 7).

When you nail this and you find and prioritize AI use cases based on the return on investment, that's when you get buy-in from all the key players.

The other side of the investment coin is the time commitment to learning about AI. Remember, you should not be and do not need to be an "expert at AI" to run AI projects: you need to know enough about it, and you should create an environment in which learning is rewarded. In a conversation I had with Paul Murphy, the CTO of GHD, a global engineering, architecture, and environmental firm, he talked about the biggest AI investment that AEC companies should make:

"Your biggest AI investment does not require extensive capital; rather, it is the investment of time and commitment to learning. Your first AI experiment will be challenging, but it will get easier as you experiment and learn more. So, you need to spend time creating a culture and a learning environment where rapid experimentation and failures get rewarded."

Now, not later

In this chapter, you have learned about AI and technology investment strategies. You have learned that it is wise to invest in AI, especially in the areas that give you market differentiation. You also learned that, to start your AI journey, you don't have to make a huge financial investment or have tons of data. Starting your AI project gives you a recipe for collecting, organizing, and nurturing your data. That's why you should invest in AI right now – before it is too late.

Unlike the adoption of CAD, BIM, and other AEC technologies, AI adoption takes a long time. Therefore, you need to invest in the time required to experiment and learn from what works and what does not work for you before you can get the full value out of the technology. Starting sooner rather than later gives you a competitive advantage in the market that is unlike any other company. James Detzel, director of innovation at Austin Commercial, a large US construction company, explains:

"Getting value from data is not a very linear process. Let's say a decade ago, when you realized that BIM and virtual design and construction were becoming important, you hired somebody who knew BIM, and that was your response to the advent of BIM – you could very quickly respond to that. But responding to data, data-driven decision-making, and getting value out of it with AI

won't be that fast. It is a different game that many companies do not realize. You need to try and experiment for a long time before you can get the value out of it. For those who have not done it, the best time to invest in data, analytics, and AI is now, before it is too late."

Act now, before it's too late.

Are you ready to embark on your AI journey? In the next part of the book, "AI Education," you'll learn about what AI is, how data is used, and some examples of AEC AI systems.

Let's go.

AN AI OPPORTUNITY

Eric Law is a senior director of innovation at Swinerton. He leads an R&D group that aims to change construction by improving schedule, cost, quality, and site safety. In a discussion that I had with him about the opportunities of using AI in AEC, he brought up several great points that I am excited to share with you below:

When I think about the AEC industry and look at the next ten years ahead of us, my biggest fear is continuing to advance at a snail's pace. The reason I'm worried is that our industry has a significant impact on society. Our operational cost impacts people's ability to afford housing, apartments, and hotels, and the cost of our operation drives all that. If we can't control those costs it's going to make it very hard to deliver the buildings that people need and the infrastructure the people deserve, and keep our countries modern and civilized. I fear that those costs will continue to rise, and our buildings and infrastructures will be just for the elite and wealthy people. We are socially responsible for stopping this from happening.

To make an equitable built environment for everyone, we should use technologies such as prefabrication, robotics, and artificial intelligence to reduce costs, schedule, and negative environmental impacts in developing buildings and infrastructure.

Among these technologies, AI has several benefits. AI provides an excellent opportunity for us to learn faster by scaling our experts' knowledge and capabilities. For instance, AI can help take the expertise of a superintendent who has many years of experience and make it accessible to hundreds of projects. Once these experts are retired from our industry, their knowledge is gone with them. AI can help us to preserve that knowledge.

Another way that AI can help us is by unboxing the learning from and success of a one-off project and making it available across a portfolio of projects. Instead of every project being a one-off success in terms of reduced cost, schedule, and an excellent product and service to the client, we can use AI to reproduce it at a larger scale.

We are dealing with the labor shortage, and AI can help us overcome that. We need to adopt robotics technologies to automate some error-prone and labor-intensive tasks in construction that drive costs.

We are in the business of design and construction, and AI is a tool in our technology toolbox. It is a powerful tool that enables us to make better decisions, solve problems, and bring down costs and schedules. It's a tool that can help us make the built environment more sustainable and equitable for everyone.

PART 2

AI Education

So what is AI really?

It may sound simple enough, but there is a lot of conflicting and misleading information out there – not to mention confusing information!

The internet is full of content about AI written by journalists and content creators, some of whom have no idea what AI is – their interaction with AI is through Hollywood movies and what they have seen in the media. Hence, first, it's important that you learn to differentiate between fact and fiction.

This part of the book will commence your AI education. You'll learn what AI is and how you can use data to add business value to your company. You will also learn about AI systems, their biases, limitations, and level of interactions. Then you will learn about three specific AEC AI systems, and how they helped leaders from Perkins & Will, McCarthy, and Swinerton to better design and build buildings.

Ready?

CHAPTER 3

Understand what AI is

Pedro went to an industry event to learn more about the application of AI in AEC. He could see so many AI-powered apps on his phone, and wondered how AI could be leveraged in his work as a designer. One of the events that he signed up for was a panel called "The Role of AI in the Future of Design and Construction." He was excited to learn more. When he arrived at the room where the event was held, he found it was packed with people who had lots of enthusiasm and energy. They all seemed to be very curious about this topic.

The moderator started the session by asking introductory questions, and later asked questions related to the application of AI in design, construction, and operation. The panelists shared lots of great ideas, from optioneering to computational and generative design to AI and machine learning. Pedro took lots of notes, and sometimes wondered what the lines between these terms were.

It was only towards the end of the panel discussion that someone asked, "Can you please define what AI is? And what's the difference between AI and machine learning or generative design?" Pedro looked around to read the room. Some folks were nodding, as if they also had the same question in their heads. Others, whose attention had drifted, stopped looking at their phones and moved their gaze to the panelist.

The first panelist gave their definition: "AI is a technology that enables us to do things that we didn't know computers could do before." The second panelist looked confused by this answer. "This is an interesting definition. Because I'm an architect, I have a slightly different definition of AI," he said. "From my point of view, generative design is AI. We use parametric design tools, which are an AI tool for design." The next panelist looked at the first two panelists as if she was not in agreement with them. "AI and machine learning are the same thing: basically, doing things in an intelligent way," she stated. All the panelists looked at each other as if no one accepted the others' definition. It was an awkward moment. The audience was confused.

Pedro thought to himself, "Everyone has been talking about AI with their own definition. If we don't have a shared understanding of what AI is, how can we use it to solve our industry problems?"

How can we leverage AI in our projects and industry if all of us have our own interpretation of what AI is and isn't?

I can relate to the story of Pedro, because many of us have sat in AI talks and meetings without having made sure that we had a shared understanding of what AI is.

The danger of learning about AI from the media is that a lot of journalists and media writers don't really know what it is. That creates a false expectation, which is dangerous. Hilda Espinal, the CTO of CannonDesign, a global architecture, engineering and consulting company, talks about the importance of AI education:

"There are a lot of misconceptions about what AI is or what it can do. Likely due to what people see in movies, media, or in games, we have developed an unrealistic expectation about what it is and

what can really be done [with it] in its current state. Often, clients and team members who are further removed from technology think that AI will completely automate complex workflows. They become disappointed when realizing that the solution developed by computation alone does not easily produce the results expected. A valuable outcome of these exercises in projects is learning what AI really is and its current, realistic state. That's why AI education is the foundation of any AI project."

This is why it's important that we spend some time understanding what AI is, and what it isn't.

What is AI really?

Believe it or not, we are surrounded by AI technology – it's everywhere. I recently had a conversation with my neighbor, who told me that he never used AI. So, I asked him to open the photo app in his iPhone and tell me how the app could automatically group all his pet photos. He looked at me and said, "So all these years, I've been using AI on my phone?" "Yes, you have," I replied.

The best way to understand what AI is and what it isn't is to look at some examples of how it is used.

AI on the road

Tesla's autonomous car uses artificial intelligence to drive itself without the need for human drivers. Each car collects a lot of data using sensors located strategically on the car that allow it to see the road, understand the context, and act based on the condition of the environment and the destination it is set to.

AI on the floor

iRobot's Roomba is used to remove debris and clean houses. Using sensors, Roomba maps your house and learns how to vacuum and clean your place without any intervention. It can detect if it is on a hardwood floor, on carpet, or near the edge of a stair. It can then act appropriately, which might be increasing the suction, reducing it, or stopping itself from falling off the cliff!

AI on TV

Netflix provides personalized movie and content selections for you to watch thanks to its AI engine, which predicts the likelihood of you wanting to watch a movie based on your past behavior and data. Netflix even personalizes the thumbnails of "Top Picks for You" based on your past interests and preferences.

AI on the shelf

Amazon's Alexa, Microsoft's Cortana, Apple's Siri, and Google Assistant are some examples of virtual assistants available on the market. You can talk to these technologies to ask questions, place orders, set reminders, get directions, and many other things.

AI in email

Gmail uses AI for spam detection, automatic classification of emails (primary, social, and promotion tabs), and autocompleting your sentences based on the content of your email and how much Google knows about you (which is a lot!).

AI in banking

The banking system uses AI to automatically flag fraudulent transactions. Based on your location, the frequency and amount of your transactions, and your pattern of use, the AI system can determine if a transaction is likely to be fraudulent or not.

AI in chatbots

Chatbots are another example of AI applications we use every day. These virtual AI agents are designed to get you the help you need as fast as possible, by either directly solving your problem or connecting you to the most relevant human assistant or customer representative.

What do all the above examples have in common? They are all AI agents. AI agents are designed to sense the environment and capture data, analyze that data to find patterns or recognize objects, and make a recommendation or initiate an action. AI agents could be a piece of software (like Alexa) or a combination of software and hardware (like autonomous cars). We interact with AI agents almost every day.

AI is all around us!

AI is like a tree

So, what is AI? Many definitions of it exist, but I lean towards a scientific definition of AI. In 1981, scientists Avron Barr and Edward A. Feigenbaum defined it as follows:

> *"Artificial Intelligence (AI) is the part of computer science concerned with designing intelligent computer systems, that is, systems that exhibit characteristics we associate with intelligence in human behavior – understanding language, learning, reasoning, solving problems, and so on."* [9]

I like this definition because it tells you that AI is a branch of science in which scientists design computer systems that mimic human intelligence.

To help you remember what AI is, I want you to think about it as a tree (see Figure 3-1). This tree has several roots: philosophy, logic and mathematics, computation, cognitive science, biology, neuroscience, and evolution. The branches of this tree are sub-fields of AI, such as computer vision, machine learning, speech recognition and synthesis, search and optimization, knowledge representation and reasoning, and robotics. Each of these branches has its own branch and sub-domain, or fields. For instance, the machine learning branch has reinforcement learning, supervised learning, and unsupervised learning as sub-branches.

AI is not magic! It has roots in various fields of science.

The roots of AI

As noted above, AI has roots in several disciplines. In philosophy, for instance, Aristotle created different styles of deductive reasoning which could generate conclusions from initial premises. A key one was the proposition, "if A implies B and A is true, then B is true" – so if, for example, dogs have four legs, and Oscar is a dog, then Oscar has four legs. Aristotle formulated this in 350 BCE, and we are still using it in AI applications today.

To take an AI precursor from another field, the biologist Charles Darwin is known for his work on evolution by natural selection. For example, he said the strongest individuals would survive and produce more of themselves. One related field of AI that emerged from this theory is called genetic programming, which is about allowing programs to evolve rather than programming them by hand.

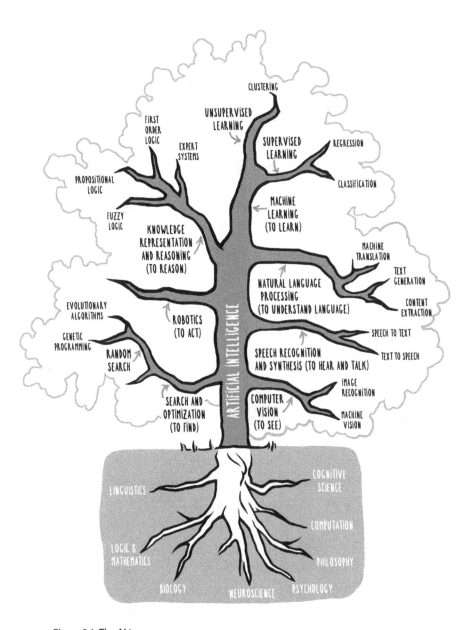

Figure 3-1: The AI tree

AI is a set of techniques and algorithms that mimic nature or human intelligence.

There are several other roots and branches of AI, but for the purposes of this book I have decided to simplify, summarize, and categorize AI to the current branches due to their popularity and relevance to AEC. In addition, in recent years various fields of AI have been merging because of the widespread use of neural networks in machine learning. For simplicity's sake, changes in these fields, as well as the relationship between these fields and their convergence, are not shown in the tree.

The branches of AI

As humans we learn new things, reason things out, accumulate knowledge, and look for the best ways we can live, work, and do things. We accomplish all of this by interacting with our environment, by communicating and talking to each other, by reading and writing, and by perceiving information. In the field of AI, scientists have tried to find out how to make computers see, hear, talk, understand language, learn, find, reason, and act the way humans do. So next, we're going to describe each of these human abilities and the fields of AI that relate to them.

Computer vision (to see)

We see the world around us through our eyes. Our brains take the electrical signals received from the retina and create images from them. In addition to creating the image, the brain can also understand what the image is, and what it is seeing in that image.

In a sub-field of AI called computer vision, computer scientists have tried to mimic how human brains perceive images by inventing techniques for computers to infer something about the world by processing image and video data (i.e., a sequence of images). Today, computer vision is being used in a variety of domains and applications, such as self-driving cars, face recognition, and monitoring people, vehicles, crops, and even farm animals.

What are the use cases for computer vision in AEC? Generally speaking, anywhere you want to extract information from images or videos taken in previous or current projects. For example, you can use it for safety inspections on site, quality control, monitoring equipment and workers, or even extracting information from designs you have done in the past (we'll learn more about these applications later). In addition to all of these use cases, computer vision could be used to create 3D models and as-builts from photos taken of a building.

If you had an AI system that could see and understand photos or videos like you do, what would you use it for?

Speech recognition and synthesis (to hear and talk)

Talking is one of the most common ways that humans communicate. We use our vocal cords to create sound signals that our brain turns into words.

In the field of speech recognition, scientists have tried to figure out how computers can convert audio signals from spoken words into written words or text (speech to text) – in other words, how they can take in what you say and automatically transcribe it. In preparation for writing this book, I interviewed several AEC experts and used some of the automated speech recognition technologies on the market (e.g., otter.ai) to automatically transcribe the interviews.

Conversely, in the field of speech synthesis, scientists have tried to see how computers can translate text into spoken words. Historically, speech synthesis techniques helped people with disabilities (most famously Stephen Hawking) to communicate with others. Today, we can see the application of speech synthesis and recognition in Amazon's Alexa, Apple's Siri, and other voice assistants.

In AEC, and generally speaking in any other domain, speech recognition and synthesis could be used to interact with computer systems. For instance, instead of typing in your report on the site or in the office, you can use your voice and speech recognition to automatically put in information. Or, instead of reading reports, you can just play and listen to them (I use Speechify for this).

If you had an AI system that could hear and talk like you do, what would you use it for?

Natural language processing (to understand language)

As humans, we learn language even before we are born. Our brain receives voice signals and, over time, learns how to perceive and comprehend language.

In the field of natural language processing (NLP), scientists have tried to make computers process, interpret, and understand human language. While you can convert your voice into text using speech recognition, the computer does not necessarily know the meaning behind the text. NLP algorithms try to determine the meaning or intention behind the text, and then take action accordingly. For instance, imagine you want to place an order on Amazon using Alexa. To do that, Alexa needs to recognize your voice, which is the field of speech recognition. It also needs to process the language and your intention behind it (i.e., placing an order). This is the natural language processing part.

In AEC, you can use NLP to process texts (e.g., requirements, building codes and regulations, project reports) and extract useful information. For instance, you can use NLP to assess the risk of your projects from the project reports or bid documents, or for code-checking and compliance requirements.

If you had an AI system that could understand textual data and language like you do, what would you use it for?

Robotics (to act)

As humans, we act or perform actions all the time, moving our body and/or objects around us without thinking too much about it. Mobility is just a natural part of us.

In the field of robotics, scientists try to create computer systems that replicate human actions. A typical robot consists of a central processing unit, sensors, actuators, end-effectors, power supply, and a control system (brain). The control system perceives the environment around it, processes data and information, makes decisions, and takes action. Two examples that I shared at the beginning of this chapter (the self-driving car and Roomba) are robots.

In AEC, robots could be used on site to perform tedious tasks and improve productivity, or in the factory to create building components and assemblies.

If you had an AI system that could act on your behalf, what would you use it for?

Machine learning (to learn)

We have all been learning things since birth. Our brain has a lot of interconnected neurons that make this learning possible. Learning is what makes us different from other animals and species. Similarly, scientists have tried to find out how a machine can learn without being explicitly programmed. This field is known as machine learning.

The field of machine learning has been growing at an unprecedented pace in the past decade, for several reasons: availability of large datasets, increased computing powers at lower cost, improved algorithms, significant investments from the public and private sectors, and so on. This growth has also helped to advance other branches of AI, such as computer vision, speech recognition and synthesis, and natural language processing. In other words, without machine learning, we would not have Siri, Alexa, or autonomous vacuum cleaners. Because of the importance of this branch of AI, I will discuss it at a slightly deeper level.

Machine learning is a branch of AI, and consists of algorithms and techniques that help computer systems learn from data, identify patterns, and make predictions or decisions without being explicitly programmed to do so.

A good example of a machine learning system that is not explicitly programmed is spam detection. There was a time when computer scientists tried to create spam filtering systems by anticipating all the rules and logic that spammers could use and programming commands to counter them – for instance, "If the email contains the word 'spam,' it is probably a spam email." But as it was impossible to catch all the tactics spammers used, the spammers were always ten steps ahead of the scientists; for example, the spammers could simply use the word "s*p*a*m" instead of "spam." So, the scientists came up with the idea of creating a dataset of spam emails and regular emails so that a computer could find these rules on its own without being explicitly programmed for those rules.

In a process that is called training, scientists provide a pair of data commonly known as input and output. The input in this case is the text in an email, and the output is whether it is a spam email or not. In AI terminology, we often call the output a "label." So, if you hear that a dataset should be labeled, it means that someone should look at each input (in this case, the email) and identify whether it is spam or not ("yes" or "no" could be the label). This labeling process happens under the supervision of a domain expert, hence the term "supervised machine learning," which is the most commonly used sub-branch of machine learning. In other words, in supervised machine learning, you need to provide a pair of inputs and labeled outputs for the machine to learn.

What does the machine learn? The algorithm that we use in the training process tries to find the mapping or relationship between the input and output. The outcome of the training process is a mathematical model that is known as a "machine learning model." In general, machine learning can be used to classify things (e.g., good email vs. spam email in Gmail), recognize objects (e.g., a human face in a photo on Facebook), make predictions based on the relationship between numbers (e.g., estimate stock prices), do something (e.g., drive an autonomous car), and generate images (create a human face).

Let's dive a little deeper now into a machine learning algorithm. One of the most-used algorithms in machine learning is called the "artificial neural network," or "neural network" for short. The idea behind the neural network is very simple. Inspired by the billions of brain cells, or neurons, that are responsible for transferring information from one side of the brain to the other, scientists thought about simulating the brain structure in computers by creating an interconnected graph with nodes and edges, or connection weights. The nodes are often stacked in different layers, such as input layer and output layer. The layers between the input and output layer are called *hidden layers*.

The number of layers in a neural network used to be small (less than five or six) because of the limitations of computing a decade ago. With the increase in computing power and the amount of data available today, we can have a deep network of these neurons (tens, hundreds, or thousands) – hence the term "deep learning." So, deep learning techniques are a subset of machine learning techniques, which are a branch of AI.

Deep learning is a sub-field of machine learning, which is a sub-field of AI.

So how does the machine learn? The training process basically involves running an optimization algorithm that tries to minimize the error of prediction between the input and output. The algorithm adjusts the weights between each node and tries to minimize the prediction error. Simply put, training a machine learning model with a neural network is an optimization problem on a network of nodes and connections. I'm sharing this level of detail so that you can understand machine learning has roots in science.

In AEC, you can use machine learning to recognize personal protective equipment, workers, or vehicles on sites, classify your photos or documents, or predict simulation, cost estimation, or your project's risk. Simply put, it can be used in all the examples that I shared in computer vision, speech recognition and synthesis, natural language processing, and robotics.

If you had an AI system that could learn to recognize objects, classify things for you, or make predictions, what would you use it for?

Knowledge representation and reasoning (to reason)

As humans, we know how to think about things in a logical way. We can form judgments or conclusions based on available facts and data. Let me give you an example. I want you to read and complete the following sentence: "Every year, we get smoke from a wildfire in July. Since it is July, we expect to..."

What was your prediction? Mine was "have wildfires." This is reasoning.

It is very important for computers to have the capability of reasoning, especially in architecture, engineering, and construction. Unlike other industries, a lot of our AEC experts are approaching retirement age, and we should find a way to capture and keep their knowledge in a form that future generations can use. But how can we represent their knowledge and use it to reason with?

One answer is creating a graph of logical statements, which is known as a knowledge graph. When you search on Google for something like, "is the Eiffel Tower in Europe?", Google looks at its knowledge graph to give you the most accurate answer. The Google knowledge graph is made of logical statements such as, "the Eiffel Tower is in Paris," and "Paris is a city in France," and "France is a country in Europe," all of which could be extracted from various sources on the Internet. To answer your question, Google's reasoning engine runs your query against the known facts to come up with an answer.

In AEC, we have a lot of rules of thumb that could be captured and used in logical form. I will give you an example. I was talking to one of the contractors of a billion-dollar project in San Francisco. One of the challenges they had was that they did not have enough time to check and validate the drawings they received every week from the architects. They told me that one of the common issues with the drawings they received was that the designers had put a deep structural beam under bathrooms. Because of the special piping and structural requirements of the project, they could not put a hole in the beam. They asked for an automated checking tool that could validate the design based on simple rules of thumb.

So, imagine that you could capture these rules of thumb – e.g., "deep structural beams should not be placed under bathrooms" – to automatically validate the building model. Or even better, instead of validation, what if you could automatically create building models based on defined design or construction rules and logic?

If you had an AI system that could capture your knowledge and reason automatically, what would you use it for?

Search and optimization (to find)

As humans, we often have multiple ways to do things. For instance, if you want to go from one city to another, you can find many different routes to get there, from highways to small, hidden roads. You can go through all the exits on the highway and come back to the highway. There are all kinds of options available to you, but most of the time, we want to find the best route or the best option.

This search problem – finding the best route or option – often has many solutions, so it is critical for a computer to be programmed in a way that can find the best options for us. Imagine you order something online, and your delivery takes 100 days because the delivery machine cannot find the fastest route to get to your house. Think about how costly it would be for the transportation agency if we did not have that capability.

So, how can computers find the best solution for us? They can do it by searching and evaluating a lot of different alternatives.

Let me give you a scenario. Imagine you want to find the best cross-section size of beams and columns for your building to match your client's limited budget. In other words, you want to minimize your construction cost (or maximize your profit), and are looking for the best columns and beams to support that. Not only that, but you also want your structural members to satisfy building code requirements, which is an optimization problem. Here, your optimization objective is to minimize the cost (or maximize your profit), your constraints are building code requirements, and your design variables (things that can change) are the size of beams and columns.

On your own, you can create one or a few design options and calculate the cost for each, and then you'll have to call it a day – you simply don't have the time to design and evaluate hundreds of options. But AI can help you with that. In this case, you can create a geometry system that can generate hundreds or thousands of solutions (known as a solution space). The role of AI would be to search that solution space and find the best design or set of designs for you.

How does AI do that?

Let me explain one of the several AI techniques which could be used to solve a search and optimization problem. Inspired by nature and how living creatures mutate and evolve over time, scientists designed evolutionary algorithms (EA). For the purpose of this book, I'll explain this without going into too much detail about EA operations such as mutation or crossover.

In the above example, the evolutionary algorithm can take control of the geometry system to generate random designs. Then it evaluates each design based on building codes and construction cost. The EA then selects the best designs and uses them to create more designs. From there, it repeats itself: it creates more designs, evaluates them based on the objective defined, takes the best ones, and creates more from the best ones. It repeats this process until there are no major improvements from one generation of design to the next.

EA is one of the optimization algorithms that could be used in computational design frameworks such as generative design. You will learn about generative design and some of the commonly used computational design terms in our industry, such as parametric design and option-eering, in the breakout story at the end of this chapter.

So, that said:

If you had an AI system that could find the best way of doing things or designing things, what would you use it for?

Let's recap what AI is. It is a field in computer science in which scientists try to build computer systems that mimic human intelligence. AI has roots in mathematics, philosophy, cognition, biology, and other scientific fields. It has various branches, such as computer vision, machine learning, speech recognition and synthesis, search and optimization, knowledge representation and reasoning, and robotics. Machine learning is a branch of AI that deals with classifying or recognizing objects and finding patterns in data.

AI or not AI? That is the question

Because of the hype (and lack of clarity) around AI, you may see some projects or products in the market that are publicized as AI-powered solutions. Seeing these, you may ask yourself, "Are these really AI-powered solutions? How can I draw a line between real AI solutions and fictitious ones?" When I asked Shane Burger, principal and global leader of technical innovation at Woods Bagot, about the importance of this distinction, he explained that:

> *"In the next ten years, my biggest fear is that there's still going to be a lot of fake AI solutions, or at least people saying that they're doing AI projects or talking about it as if they are, but in reality,*

they are not doing any AI project. So, it's crucial to know how we can catch the fake AI claims."

How can you do that? The answer is by looking for any of the branches of the AI tree in the project or product – and, if you can't find one, asking questions of the technology solution providers. For instance, if someone says they have AI software that generates thousands of building geometries in one second, you should immediately think (or ask questions) about the branches of the AI tree that this tool may use. Let's say you land on optimization; from here, you should find the answers to questions like, "What type of optimization algorithm is used?" or, "What are the optimization goals or constraints?" If you cannot find any branch of the AI tree or there is no AI algorithm used in the tool, then it is not using AI.

By looking for branches of the AI tree and asking relevant questions, you can quickly draw a line between real AI solutions and fictitious ones.

Let's review

Let's go back to story of Pedro at the beginning of the chapter and think about some of the statements that were made about AI:

- "AI is a technology that enables us to do things that we didn't know computers could do before."
- "Generative design is AI."
- "We use parametric design tools, which are an AI tool for design."

- "AI and machine learning are the same thing: basically, doing things in an intelligent way."

Now pause for a moment, and, based on what you have learned so far, see if you can identify which statements are correct and which are not.

Got it yet? The answer is, none of them – the first one is too generic, and the rest of them are incorrect. Let's take a look at each one in turn.

- "AI is a technology that enables us to do things that we didn't know computers could do before."

This statement could be applied to other technologies that are not necessarily AI. A lot of technologies have helped us to do things with computers that we couldn't do before, but are fundamentally not AI technologies – think of the internet, virtual reality, or 3D printing.

- "Generative design is AI."

Here, you are comparing apples to oranges. Generative design is a design framework that may or may not use AI techniques (e.g., optimization techniques inspired by biology). In other words, you may create a design solution using a generative design framework without utilizing any branches of AI. You will learn more about generative design from John Haymaker, director of research at Perkins & Will, later in this chapter.

- "We use parametric design tools, which are an AI tool for design."

In the "AI or not AI" section above, you learned that when you see or hear about an AI-powered tool, you should immediately think about the AI tree and ask yourself which techniques or branches of it are being used. So, ask yourself: "Which branches of the AI tree are used when geometry is modeled and created parametrically?" I often can't find any, can you? You can often create millions of designs with parametric modeling and scripting techniques without any use of AI.

- "AI and machine learning are the same thing: basically, doing things in an intelligent way."

No, they are not. One reason I want you to remember the tree is that people often use the terms "machine learning" and "AI" interchangeably. But this is not correct: machine learning is a sub-field of AI. All machine learning techniques are AI techniques, but not all AI techniques are machine learning techniques.

Think about AI as a house and machine learning as a room in the house – that's the difference.

How to use AI to solve AEC problems

In the previous chapter, you learned about the 3P challenges (pressure, productivity, profitability) as well as the opportunities for using AI. Now that you know what AI is and is not, let's discuss two main ways you can use AI to solve AEC problems.

In general, you can use AI to solve your problems either by modeling the problem (let's call this a modeling-based approach) or providing lots of examples or data (let's call this a learning-based approach). For instance, let's say you decide to use AI to increase your productivity in designing the layouts of commercial buildings. Using the modeling-based approach, you need to model your problem to a computer system, which involves creating a representation of the building geometry (i.e., geometry system) and defining the logic behind how you design the layout (e.g., design principles, rules of thumb, building codes, client requirements). For instance, your AI algorithm can use a predefined rule such as "external meeting rooms should be placed close to the entrance" to generate floor-plan layouts. The branches of the AI tree used in this approach are "search and optimization" and "knowledge-based and reasoning."

Using the learning-based approach, you need to have or generate many building layout examples – more than 10,000, and ideally around 100,000. Each building layout should be labeled with the name of each room (e.g., external meeting room, entrance, bathroom). Your AI algorithm then uses this data to find the patterns in your past designs and the relationship between building entities. For instance, if there are enough examples in which the external meeting rooms were placed close to the entrance, you'll see in the solutions the algorithm generates that they are placed close to each other. This means that your AI solution learned the rule "external meeting rooms should be placed close to the entrance" from your data without you explicitly defining it. The main branch of the AI tree used in this approach is "machine learning."

As mentioned in the previous section, machine learning techniques (which require lots of data) are entangled with all other branches of the AI tree. That's why, more than ever, your data is vital in solving problems. In the next chapter, you'll learn more about data and its five characteristics.

KEY TAKEAWAYS

- AI is a branch of science.
- AI has roots in various scientific fields, such as philosophy, logic and mathematics, computation, cognitive science, biology, neuroscience, and evolution.
- Some of the sub-fields of AI are computer vision, machine learning, speech recognition and synthesis, search and optimization, knowledge representation and reasoning, and robotics.
- Generative design is not AI – it is a design framework.
- Generative design may or may not use AI techniques such as evolutionary algorithms.
- Similarly, parametric design tools often do not use AI techniques in solving design problems.
- AI agents (e.g., self-driving cars) seem to be intelligent because they can mimic human capabilities.

AI IN DESIGN

Dr. John Haymaker is the director of research at Perkins & Will, a global design company. John is an architect by training and has spent his design career working for owners, contractors, and architecture firms. He has also taught architecture and civil engineering at the Georgia Institute of Technology and Stanford University. In my discussion with John, he talked about the role of AI in design, and I'd like to share what he said:

I view design as decision-making. To design, you need to gather decision-makers, establish constraints and goals for the decision, create potential solutions, analyze the trade-offs between the answers based on the requirements, and then decide the answer. For instance, you go through this process to decide on the building volume, and then go through it again to design the building core or the façade. We used to do all these steps manually, but nowadays we use computers, hence the term 'computational design.'

Under the umbrella of computational design, we have different terminologies, such as parametric design, optioneering, and generative design. Let me briefly explain each of these terms.

Parametric design is a form of design where designers create potential solutions by defining fixed and changeable parameters, or variables, and their relationships. For instance, in designing a façade, we can identify the four corners of the façade as fixed and define some movable control points for creating the curvature in the geometry. Using parametric technology tools, you can define these parameters and their relationship to create design solutions.

You can connect your parametrically defined geometry (or parametric model) to a code or script to create thousands of options automatically, hence the term 'optioneering'. With the goal of finding a high-performing design solution, you need to calculate the performance of the options generated. Therefore, you should connect your geometry generation routine (let's call it a geometry engine) to an evaluator or performance simulation engine (e.g., structure, energy, daylighting, cost) to assess any design metrics you have (e.g., cost, view, esthetic).

Because these calculations are time-consuming, you cannot just randomly create design geometries and simulate them. In other words, you need to control how the geometry generation engine creates designs, and point it in the direction of generating more high-performing solutions. That's where we need to layer other algorithms on top. The algorithm needs to create various solutions automatically, measure their performance, analyze the trade-offs, and guide the geometry engine to create high-performing or better solutions. This is what is known as generative design today.

We can choose to use AI algorithms in generative design or not. For instance, you can choose to formulate it as a search and optimization problem and use evolutionary algorithms to generate, mutate, and select geometry. Or, we can use learning-based algorithms to quickly generate geometry based on patterns in data or measure the performance of buildings for energy, daylighting, or structure.

AI is not generative design, and generative design is not AI. You can choose to use AI algorithms in generative design.

It's up to us to define the future of design with AI. Instead of codifying existing processes and practices that emphasize only efficiency, we should enable architects to create innovative and transcendent solutions using the power of AI. An AI technology that asks questions wisely frames problems differently and helps architects see the world differently. Design is not a destination: it's a journey in which we make lots of decisions. And we want AI to be part of that journey by guiding and coaching us to make better decisions, rather than showing us one possible destination.

CHAPTER 4

Identify how data is used

It was a beautiful day in London. I was there to visit some customers to find out how AI could help their businesses and projects. I scheduled lunch with Erin, the CEO of a construction company, to learn more about her data challenges and strategy.

"Data is gold," Erin told me, "and my strategy is to capture as much of it as possible. But I don't think we are doing enough. Our design and construction team generate terabytes of data every day. I told my CIO that we should capture and store all this data because it might be useful in future AI projects. Wouldn't you agree?"

I didn't know what to say. For a long time, I've been hearing variations of this statement: "Data is the new oil" or "the new electricity," "Data is the future," and so on. But nobody defines what data is or what type of data is oil or electricity.

I gently replied, "Lots of companies gather unorganized data without knowing what they're capturing it for. Without knowing what you want to do with data and setting some goals and expectations, you don't know how to capture, nurture, and clean your data."

"Let me give you an example," I continued. "Let's say that in the past five years, you have been storing all your building models. You keep thinking, 'I'm going to use it for something one day.' And imagine one day, after five years of data collection, you want to use it to create an AI agent that takes in client requirements, zoning requirements, building codes, and so on, in order to construct a building geometry based on all the designs that you have in your database.

"At that moment, when you have a specific goal in mind, you'll realize that your data is not good for that purpose and there are lots of gaps. For instance, the link between the building models and the code or client requirements used to create the building model might be missing. When you realize what you want to do with your data, you can identify where the gaps are and what and how you should capture, nurture, and clean your data. As Stephen R. Covey, author of *The 7 Habits of Highly Effective People*, points out, you should 'Begin with the end in mind.'"

Capture data with the end in mind.

"What do you mean by nurture or clean your data? Can't AI just do it for us?" Erin asked.

To put things in perspective, I used a metaphor:

"Let's assume that your business is like a sports car. As a CEO, you are the car's driver, and you want to take the car to a destination faster than your competitors. You want to win the race that you are in. Your data is the car's fuel. You need to create a system or a process by which your team can capture the fuel, clean it, and purify it based on the specifications of your AI engine. Some engines can handle not-so-pure fuel, but others need a specific level of purity. Your AI engine consumes this fuel and generates forces and acceleration that can propel you to go faster and better in the market than all your other competitors. These forces and accelerations are business values."

Your business is like a sports car, and AI is the engine that converts your cleaned data into forces and acceleration that propel your business to go faster and better in the market than all your competitors.

I should have shared my grocery-shopping metaphor that I told you about in Chapter 2 with Erin, but I hadn't come up with it at that time. Regardless, Erin was very happy with the sports-car metaphor, and at the end of our session she concluded, "Capturing lots and lots of data without having any specific goal or purpose leads to a waste of time and money, and creates re-work in the future."

To avoid all of these pitfalls, I have dedicated this chapter to data. You have lots of data in your company that could be turned into business value using machine learning and other AI or statistical techniques, so it is crucial to learn and develop a multifaceted view of your data. That's why, in this chapter, you will learn what data is, what its five characteristics are, some of your data challenges, and what the first step in governing your data is.

To begin, let's talk about what data is.

What is data?

Think about data as a snapshot of the physical world at a given time. As humans, we capture data using sensory organs in our body such as our eyes, ears, nose, tongue, and skin. This raw data is then processed by our brain to become information. For instance, imagine that you are watching a sunset. The image of the sunset that you see is data, but processing it and labeling it as "beautiful" is information.

Every day we experience the world based on many observations drawn from a map of the world inside our brain. What we know about the world is a collection of these experiences, beliefs, and observations, which we call "knowledge." Knowledge is what we know about the world, and it is stored (you guessed it) inside our brain. What we have inside our brain is not the physical world itself: it is a *map* or replica, constantly evolving every day as new observations or experiences come in.

Data is a collection of facts and observations from the world.
Information is processed data.
Knowledge is interconnected observations and beliefs about the world.

To summarize, data is a collection of facts, observations, or events in the forms of numbers, dates, time, and text. Processing data creates useful information, and processing such information generates knowledge.

To give you a better way to think about data, I'll discuss what is known as the "5 Vs" of data in the following section (see Figure 4-1). These 5 Vs are usually discussed in big-data communities, but are applicable to any type of dataset you may have in your company, however big or small. Then I will briefly talk about data challenges and governance, and how you can take your first step in organizing your data at your company level.

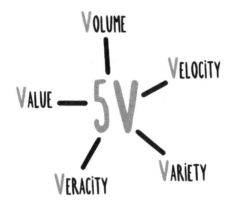

Figure 4-1: The five characteristics of data (the 5 Vs)

Five characteristics of data (5 Vs)

1. Volume (scale of data)

Volume refers to the size and amount of data that is collected.

Year after year, your company captures and generates more data in your internal and/or external servers. This is the data that can shape your company's future, so you should be mindful of the scale of data in your business.

*What is the volume of data in your organization
year after year in the past ten years?*

2. Velocity (speed of data generation)

Velocity is the speed at which data is being generated and moved. Some data comes in real time, and some data comes in batches.

There is a correlation between the velocity of data and the business case for using it. For instance, imagine you designed an AI application for automatically monitoring the safety of construction

workers on site. The app informs the safety manager if a worker vio-
lates a safety regulation. On one hand, you need high-velocity data
and must stream video recordings to capture the safety violations
in real time. On the other hand, you may want to capture data such
as the temperature of your construction sites, which you don't necessarily need to track and record every second or every minute. For
cases such as this, low-velocity data could be sufficient.

Does your data velocity match your business use cases?

---

3. Variety (forms of data)

You can think about variety of data in three different ways. The first
is the type or forms of data that you can store in your computer or
database (e.g., photos, videos, GPS data, PDFs, documents).

The second way of looking at variety in your data is how structured
or unstructured your data is. Structured data is data that is organized
to fit, for instance, into a table or a relational database application. This
type of data is more suitable for data analytics and machine learning
training than unstructured data. Some examples of unstructured data
are photos, videos, PDFs, audio or text files, books, and emails.

The third way of looking at variety of data is how that data is created.
There are more than three ways of generating data, but for simplicity's
sake I will limit it to three: 1) sensory data (data generated by sensors),
2) human-created data (data created by humans), and 3) synthetic data
(data generated by algorithms).

1. **Sensory data:** a sensor is a device that converts observations
   from the physical world into digital formats – it's a data-gener-
   ation machine! For example, a sensor in a camera converts the
   light (photons) environment into a signal (a sequence of discrete

values) that can be understood by machines and humans. Another example is a proximity sensor, which detects the presence of an object or living being when it enters the sensor's field. Some examples of sensory data are photos, videos, GPS, proximity data, and weather data.

2. **Human-created data:** as the name suggests, this data is created by humans. This could be data about your current or past projects, architectural design or engineering design, or data about the site, local codes, project-specific information, stakeholders, suppliers, and so on.

3. **Synthetic data:** capturing real-world data with sensors is often complex, and takes time. Or sometimes, we don't have enough past-project data. In cases such as these, we use computers to create a synthetic dataset. For instance, if you wanted to measure the stress applied to the piers of a pedestrian bridge, you could either install various vibration and strain sensors and accelerometers on the bridge to capture data in a year, *or* create a dataset using finite element analysis software in combination with your computer. To generate synthetic data, you often need to randomly sample a space of possible solutions (e.g., various types of loads or bridge geometries). Therefore, it is critical to make sure that all the permutations are feasible and valid in real-world projects. For instance, a highway bridge with a pier height of ten centimeters is not a valid bridge, and should be removed from the dataset. Otherwise, the value and quality of your dataset would be minimal.

Understanding data variety is significant in your AI journey. If you lack data in certain areas, you can generate it using one of the three ways shared in this section.

How can you make your unstructured data more structured and ready for your AI projects?

---

4. Veracity (quality of data)

Veracity refers to the quality of your data and, in general, how much trust you have in your data. In one of my past projects, we wanted to create a digital twin of a car chassis. The goal of the project was to capture sensor data on how the car was being utilized so as to algorithmically design the next version of it. My job was to analyze the sensor data and develop AI algorithms that could design the next version of the car.

I was not involved in the project's data-collection phase, during which one mechanical and two electrical engineers installed thirty-six sensors on the chassis and collected data over a period of time. A few weeks later, I received terabytes of data, but did not know where each of the thirty-six sensors was installed on the chassis, as the engineers had forgotten to capture and record the location of sensors. We could calculate stress and strain on the chassis based on the data we received, but we didn't have any information about where the stress and strain were applied. So, we had terabytes of low-quality data that nobody could trust, and thus had to redo the experiment.

Another way of looking at the quality of your data is how relevant or out of date your data is. For some data, like building design, the codes and requirements change every few years, which means that a building designed twenty years ago may not comply with the codes and standards of today because those requirements have changed.

You've probably heard the saying "garbage in, garbage out." If your data doesn't have good quality, you won't get the results you expect. So, you really need to think about the quality of your data when you are capturing and maintaining it.

How much trust do you have in your data?

5. Value of data

What is the value that data brings to your organization? The answer to this question is directly related to the business problem that you have at hand. So, think about the business value that you can create if you solve the problem and find out how data, analytics, and AI can help. In other words, you should not just capture data because everybody is doing it: you should be strategic about it. You need to start with your business questions or the problems you have, and then find (or generate) data to answer those questions or solve those problems.

What is the business question that can guide your data collection?

Now that we understand the five characteristics of data, let's move on to discussing how to get value out of that data.

Get value from your data with analytics and AI

But before we talk about how to extract value from your data, let's talk about what types of questions could be answered by data analytics and AI.

In a discussion I had with Niels W. Falk, CEO of HD Lab, he shared this with me:

"To run any project, you need to know what has been done, what is going on now, and what needs to be done and how. Without

analyzing data, you won't know what has been done, what is going on, and what needs to be done in the design and construction of projects."

What is the business value of your data?

To do this, you need to run various types of analytics on your data, such as descriptive, diagnostic, predictive, and prescriptive. These data analytics are shown in Figure 4-2. Let's take a closer look at each of them.

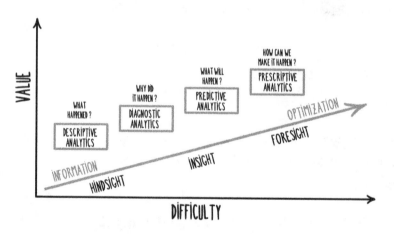

Figure 4-2: Gartner's analytic value escalator (source: Gartner.com)

- **Descriptive analytics:** to answer the questions "What happened in the past?" or "What is happening now?"

When I talk to business executives in AEC, I often hear that they are creating dashboards for their companies using tools like Microsoft Power BI. I like this tactic because it helps them to organize and centralize their data. For example, you can use descriptive analysis to create a pie chart of your projects based on their locations (e.g., 50% in North America, 30% in Europe, and 20% in Asia) or create a report on how many of your projects have delays.

- **Diagnostic analytics:** to answer the question "Why did it happen?"

Sometimes you want to understand the root cause of certain things that happened in your project or business. Diagnostic analytics can show you why the event happened by using techniques like data mining or correlation analysis. For example, you can run diagnostic analysis on your projects to find why some of your projects had delays or low profit margins.

- **Predictive analytics:** to answer the question "What will happen?"

In this type of analytics, you try to predict what is likely to happen based on your historical data. But this type of analytics cannot predict the future – no one can! What it does is find the pattern in data to forecast a potential future outcome. For example, based on all the projects that you have won in the past, you can create a predictive model that can tell you how much you should bid on a new project. You can use AI techniques such as supervised machine learning to create your forecast model and find the price that can increase your chances of winning the project. But, of course, there is no guarantee that you actually *will* win the project.

- **Prescriptive analytics:** to answer the questions "How can we make it happen?" or "What can we do?"

With prescriptive analytics, you can run what-if scenarios for your project or business – for example, "What happens if the project is two days delayed?" or "What happens if we lease the formwork instead of buying it?" or "What happens if we build the structure with concrete instead of steel?" You can use AI techniques such as optimization and machine learning to answer these questions.

As you can see in Figure 4-2, the value and difficulty of analytics increases from left to right.

It is important to note that both descriptive and diagnostic analysis is usually done using various statistical analysis techniques that are not related to AI. Having said that, these analyses are crucial for understanding your data and avoiding potential biases in your AI solutions (you'll learn more about biases in AI systems in the next chapter). To do predictive and prescriptive analysis, you need to use AI techniques such as reasoning, optimization, and machine learning, all of which are covered in this book.

With the power of AI and your data about what happened in the past, you can create potential future scenarios and enhance the chances of making them happen.

A misconception about the analytics graph in Figure 4-2 that is held by some of the business executives I talk to is that these are steps that should be taken one after the other: "First, I need to prepare my data for descriptive analysis, which may take a couple or several years. Then I need to go to diagnostic analysis, and so on." This is not true. This graph is just a guide. As discussed earlier, you should always ask yourself, "What is the business problem that I have or what is the opportunity that I want to create for my company?" The answer to this question is your starting point.

Data challenges in AEC

Now that you know about the characteristics of data and the values that AI can bring to your company (at least on an abstract level), it's time to dig into some of the challenges you may have with your data.

Why challenges?

The amount of data that is being produced year after year is increasing at an exponential rate. According to Daniel Price from Cloudtweaks. com:

> *"The amount of data is growing exponentially. Today, our best estimates suggest that at least 2.5 quintillion bytes of data is produced every day (that's 2.5 followed by a staggering 18 zeros!)."*

This trend is the same for the AEC industry. Digitization of design, construction, and operation is bringing more and more data to AEC companies every day; having cameras and other sensory devices installed during and after construction generates lots of data for designers, contractors, and owners. Here is a list of some of the challenges with data in AEC:

- **Data silo:** you use different, disconnected tools for design, construction, and running the back end of your business. Each of these tools has its own file format and is stored independently in different parts of your organization.
- **No standard or policy:** your teams have their own logic to capture, process, and store data. As a result, the data quality is diminished, and it's been challenging for you and your team to trust the data and leverage it to ensure effective decisions.
- **No context around the stored data:** since data is scattered all over the place and the relationships between various datasets are broken, you miss the context around data. For instance, you

may have twenty different design revisions in a project, but you cannot find the revision specifications and requirements linked to them.

- **Unstructured data:** your team stores unstructured data (e.g., images, videos, audio and text files, PDFs) without proper organization or absent metadata or labeling, not knowing that creating business values out of unstructured datasets is extremely difficult.

Therefore, handling all these data sources, processing the data, and making it ready for AI and analytics becomes a sizable challenge.

What are your biggest data challenges?

So how can you align your organization to do that? The answer is by having data governance.

Data governance

I was consulting for a design company to train a machine learning model that could generate design drawings. Their biggest problem was the quality of the designs developed. They put most of their efforts into correcting the machine learning model, but the cause of the problem was something else.

Because three different people were involved in collecting, cleaning, and labeling the data, there was a significant quality issue in the dataset due to inconsistency. One architect drew red rectangles around the bathrooms and labeled them as "bath"; the second drew white rectangles and labeled them as "washroom," and the third one something else. As you want all of the labels to be the same (same color, shape, wording, etc.) in order for the machine learning model to function properly, I put together a guideline for labeling and preparing the drawings and asked the architects to follow the guideline. The result? Significant improvement in the quality of the output.

But how can you implement this type of guidance at the company level? This is where data governance comes in. (Please note that data governance is not the subject of this book, and many books are written about this subject. However, I will briefly explain what it is below.)

Simply put, data governance is a set of strategies, rules, procedures, policies, and accountability guidelines for the management of data assets in your company. Data governance brings transparency to how data is being processed, establishes who is accountable for which data-related processes, lessens the friction between team members, and brings a systematic approach to your company. In general, it increases the quality of your data and helps you and your business make better decisions while reducing the cost of data management.

The difference between data governance and data management is that data governance focuses on developing policies, standards, and guidelines, and ensuring they are followed. Data management, meanwhile, is a business function that focuses on executing these policies and standards.

What is the first step that you can take in organizing your data?

The first step is working with team members from different areas of your organization to come up with a common data definition. To see how Suffolk, a multibillion-dollar construction company, has done this, I reached out to Jit Kee Chin, the company's chief data and innovation officer. Before concluding this chapter, I'd like to share her advice:

"One of the first steps in creating reliable data governance is agreeing on a common definition of data because, ultimately, you want to use your data to make critical decisions. So, different functions and departments of a company need to define the data that needs

to be captured. For instance, you want to capture data related to your projects. But, what is the definition of a project? For example, let's say you won a mega-project and split that into three projects. With your team, you need to discuss and define if you have one or three projects.

"This can be applied at different levels, depending on business needs. For example, within a project, we can choose to capture 3D models, financial information, schedules, safety information, insurance, and claims, among others. Drill down another level, and we can define the sub-components of each dataset. For instance, for safety, you may choose to capture weather information, type and severity of accidents, type of activity engaged in, trade-partner type, and so on. Again, everything that you are going to capture should be clearly defined and agreed upon. Once this is done, systematically implementing these definitions, and ensuring high data quality, will greatly increase the value of the information.

"The benefits of having good data governance are huge. Our industry has many different functional tools and software that hold and lock information for that specific function (e.g., construction document management, BIM, financials, schedule), but they don't interoperate. Therefore, you often cannot tie different types of project information together and see the impact of upstream changes on downstream tasks. Implementing data governance helps you unlock your data to see how your upstream decisions might influence something downstream."

How do you govern your data? What are the policies, guidelines, and frameworks that you have in place at the company level? How do you make sure that they are executed consistently?

To summarize, your data governance provides policies, guidelines, and a unified approach to capture, nurture, and organize your data in a way that is consumable by statistical and AI techniques. With these, you can turn your data into information and knowledge and bring tremendous value to your company.

KEY TAKEAWAYS

- Data is the collection of facts and observations from the world.
- The 5 Vs of data are: volume (scale of data), velocity (speed of data generation), variety (forms of data), veracity (quality of data), and value of data.
- Descriptive analytics answers the questions "What happened in the past?" or "What is happening now?"
- Diagnostic analytics answers the question "Why did it happen?"
- Predictive analytics answers the question "What will happen?"
- Prescriptive analytics answers the questions "How can we make it happen?" or "What can we do?"
- Data governance is a set of strategies, rules, procedures, policies, and accountability guidelines for the management of data assets in your company.
- One of the first steps in creating reliable data governance is agreeing on a common definition of data, such as "project."

ACT NOW!

Nick Bagatelos was the president of Bagatelos Architectural Glass Systems (BAGS) for thirty-two years. BAGS designs, engineers, and manufactures unitized curtain wall units in Sacramento, California. To improve the glass performance by 600%, he recently started a new company called Lux Wall to build a tempered vacuum-insulated glass manufacturing facility in Michigan. I recently had a conversation with Nick about how data generates value for BAGS. Here is what he told me:

Construction has such a significant impact on the economy, on our safety, health, and comfort. One of my biggest fears for the industry is the slow pace of change. If the industry doesn't change, it will become more expensive for us to heat and cool our buildings. So, it'll be hard for people's lives to get better.

One of the changes that I brought into Bagatelos Architectural Glass was introducing a unified data solution that ties our design, engineering, manufacturing, and installation processes together. There are so many tools in the market that have thousands of features that we don't need. I knew from experience that we need to be tech provider-agnostic and build our own solution.

Our data platform connects the geometry of our unitized system to the engineering, manufacturing, and installation process, including time and cost. We created a closed-loop system to bring lessons learned from each project into this data platform to get better over time.

Our ultimate goal is to use data and the power of analytics and AI to know what has been done, the current status, and what needs to be done to complete a job successfully. For instance, we can color-code each curtain wall unit based on its engineering, manufacturing, and installation status: green means 'complete', yellow means 'currently in progress', and red means 'have not started yet'. This visualization engine makes our communication across various organizations so much easier.

As part of our conversation, I asked Nick to explain the value of each type of analytics as he experienced it in his company.

Descriptive Analytics - What happened?
"The value of descriptive analysis and analyzing our past data is finding places where we made mistakes and bringing those learnings into our closed-loop system. Knowing that we won't make the same mistake twice gives us confidence and reliability on our job sites. Since we don't have to be worried about liabilities, we can slightly reduce our margins, improving our revenue."

Diagnostic Analytics - Why did it happen?
"We use diagnostic analytics to understand why we lose money on some of our projects or don't hit the expected margin on the project. Sometimes it is because of external factors, but sometimes it is internal factors such as poor management or team performance. The only way to get better is to know why it happened."

Predictive Analytics - What will happen?
"We can use predictive analytics and the power of AI to predict the risk of a project based on the current progress. If the prediction shows that the project risk is high because of delays in some parts of the process, we try to reduce the risk by adding more manpower.

This is how we eliminate the risk and uncertainties from our projects."

Prescriptive Analytics - How can we make it happen?

"We can use prescriptive analytics to identify what needs to be done when our installation schedule changes. In some of our projects, one week before installing our units, the general contractor tells us that the edge of the slab won't be ready because another subcontractor has not completed the job. For example, instead of the south side, we should install the units on the north side of the building, but some of the curtain wall units on the north side might be different. We need to stop our engineering and manufacturing operations and redo our release packages, which is extremely difficult. We can use AI to create various options and alternatives so we can make it happen.

"Where are we with our data and AI project? We're in the middle of the journey. And I don't think this journey has a destination, because as the tools get better you need to learn and improve yourself, your factory, and your staff, and take those enhancements back to your tools. This is a continuous learning and improvement journey. If you stop, you'll be irrelevant.

"The benefit we gained from our digital transformation journey has been tremendous. Reducing repetitive tasks and performing rapid and accurate engineering and pricing could significantly improve our bottom line.

"My advice to other business executives is to get on the data and AI wagon before it is too late. If you want your company to thrive and grow, you must make the digital transition in the next several years; otherwise, you're going to fail. If you are happy with not growing and want to retire in the next five years, then wait and see what happens. But if you want to grow and have a viable business in a decade, you must act *now!*"

CHAPTER 5

Know what AI systems are

"When you think about artificial intelligence, what are the thoughts or questions that come to your mind?" I ask this question a lot when I kick off a workshop or a conference keynote. Usually, I hear answers like: "excited," "can't wait to learn more about it," "AI is changing our lives." But I remember a cold winter day in Indianapolis when the answers were a bit different. I had a workshop with twenty architecture, engineering, and construction professionals, but on that day my audience was very different from the usual millennial crowd: instead, they were baby-boomer executives and managers with many years of professional experience in AEC. I could not see any sign of excitement from them. Everyone was silent for a minute or two after I asked the question. It was as if they'd heard nothing, or didn't know how to respond.

All of a sudden, someone yelled from the back of the room: "AI is taking over. AI is here to take our jobs and send everybody home." I was shocked, but tried to have empathy and see these answers from their point of view. So I smiled and said, "Thanks for sharing that; any other thoughts?" I was hoping that someone had something positive to say. A middle-aged person with gray hair raised his hand. I nodded and said, "Please." He said, "AI is for universities, not for the construction industry." Other people in the crowd started nodding as if they agreed with him. The two students in the front row looked at each other and chuckled as the flow of comments from the older attendees kept coming. "AI will take my job"; "We put bricks on top of each other; how does AI help with that?" someone said sarcastically. "Will we need architects ten years from now? Because AI is taking architects' jobs," others shouted.

It was an awkward moment, and I still think about that workshop.

It made me realize that there is a huge learning gap between what AI really does and what is pictured in the media and news.
Hence, there is (understandably) a lot of misunderstanding around it.

Some people feel excited by the prospect of all the things AI can do, but others are scared because it's a foreign language, not much is out there, or the media makes it seem that "the robots are taking our jobs." One way to close the learning gap between what AI really does and what is said about it in media and news is learning about AI-powered computer solutions (or AI systems). That's why, in this chapter, you'll learn what AI systems are and about the misconceptions surrounding them. Then, you'll learn about interacting with them, and about their inherent limitations and biases.

What is an AI system?

Let me explain AI systems by reintroducing what AI agents are. In Chapter 3, you learned that we deal with AI agents every day in banking, customer support (e.g., chatbot), or checking our email. An AI agent is an AI-powered computer program that can sense the environment with sensors, process the data received from the environment, and use

AI algorithms to recommend an action or act on behalf of a human (see Figure 5-1).

Let's use cars as an example. A self-driving car captures road conditions, signs, and other information from the environment, processes the data, and accelerates, decelerates, keeps going at the same speed, or stops based on the conditions observed. The car is an AI agent. The combination of the AI agent and the environment that the agent is perceiving information from and acting on is called an AI system. In the rest of the book, I use the terms AI agent and AI system interchangeably.

An AI agent is an autonomous entity that has two main functions: perceiving the environment via sensors, and acting on that environment via actuators.

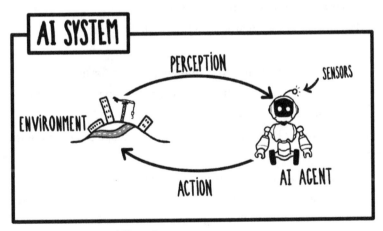

Figure 5-1: AI system and AI agent

AI agents are not programmed to do specific tasks. They sense the environment to capture and process data to recommend an action or act automatically.

An AI agent could also be a piece of software like Netflix's or Amazon's recommendation engines. In this case, the AI agent captures data from the customers' behavior (e.g., movies watched or items bought), analyzes the data, and uses AI to recommend new movies or similar items to buy.

Now that you know what AI agents and systems are, let's discuss the sources of misconceptions about AI systems and how to avoid them.

Misconceptions about AI systems

To understand the root cause of misconceptions about AI systems, I conducted three days of research about AI and the future of AEC in an industry gathering. The question I asked was, "When you think about the future of AI and AEC, what do you see ten years from now?" After completing the exercise and analyzing data, I found two main emotional categories for all responses received: excitement or fear.

Here are some comments from the excited people:

- "I can see a day when AI is doing the design for us; it reads the project brief, talks to the client, and comes up with the project's design really quickly."
- "Submitting RFIs, managing change orders, and dealing with issues will be wholly automated by AI."
- "Autonomous cars will bring the materials or modular building components to the site, and robots will assemble them. So, we won't even need skilled workers."

And here are some comments from people who expressed their fear about AI and the future of the AEC industry:

- "In ten years, AI will design, build, and operate buildings for us. This will be the end of my profession as a designer."

- "I don't see myself building buildings the way I do today, because people will be able to order buildings on Amazon that will be designed, customized, and delivered for Prime members in two days."
- "AI will completely handle building operations."

Which category of answers do you think are true? The answer is neither. Both categories of responses are unrealistic!

After doing more research, I found three root causes of our AI misconceptions. The first two are caused by our mind: we attribute human-level intelligence to AI systems, and then generalize what they are capable of. Media is the source of the third one: we only see and hear the success stories, and don't learn about situations in which an AI system does not work.

Let's talk about each of these misconceptions in detail.

Misconception 1: Attributing human-level intelligence to AI systems

Believe it or not, we get fooled very easily by machines. Back in 2016, when Google's DeepMind team developed an AI system (AlphaGo) that could beat Lee Sedol, one of the world's best Go champions, many people thought AI agents were becoming more intelligent than humans. But as Gary Marcus and Ernest Davis note in their book *Rebooting AI: Building Artificial Intelligence We Can Trust*:

> *"Just because something manages to appear intelligent for a moment or two doesn't mean that it really is, or that it can handle the full range of circumstances a human would."* [10]

So, in the AlphaGo example, the AI system was able to beat a human in that specific game, but it does not mean that it can think or handle the many different, complex things that humans can. For example, in my three-day research that I mentioned at the beginning of this section, one of the executives of a design company asked me, "Why doesn't AI read all the building codes and come up with a perfect design solution for us?" When I told him AI systems can *mimic* reading but cannot read as humans do, he frowned. I explained it like this: let's say you read a story that starts with, "I was thirsty and dragging my feet along the sand while waves were breaking on the beach." When you're reading this text, your brain creates a cognitive model that not only knows all the objects and contents of the story, but also knows their connections, the context, and the point being made. Also, your brain maps this model to all your past experiences (e.g., being on a beach on a sunny day, or getting dehydrated). These are just some of the activities that automatically happen in your brain when you read. Therefore, because of their lack of cognitive abilities, the most advanced AI systems cannot read as humans do.

But why do we think they can read, write, listen, or learn? Because they are machines, and they mimic what we, as humans, do. So, we overestimate their abilities and attribute more to them than they are capable of. As Gary Marcus and Ernest Davis explain:

> "We humans did not evolve to distinguish between humans and machines – which leaves us easily fooled. We attribute intelligence to computers because we have evolved and lived among human beings who themselves base their actions on abstractions like ideas, beliefs, and desires. The behavior of machines is often superficially similar to the behavior of humans, so we are quick to attribute to machines the same sort of underlying mechanisms, even when they lack them." [10]

The victory of AlphaGo in the Go game doesn't mean that computers are brilliant. So, next time that you talk to Siri or Alexa, try not to give them too much credit for being as intelligent as a human.

Because AI systems mimic some core human functions, we overestimate their capabilities and attribute to them more than what they can really do.

Misconception 2: Generalizing the capabilities of AI systems

It is very important to know the type of problems that AI technology can solve. We can organize the problems in the world into two categories: wicked and tame.

The term "wicked problem" was introduced in the mid-1960s by Horst Rittel and Melvin Webber, professors at the University of California, Berkeley, in their paper "Dilemmas in a general theory of planning" [11]. A wicked problem is a problem that is not well understood and is subject to change. In these problems, the definitions and rules are fuzzy, definitions can change at any time, and the problems and their solutions are open to interpretation. Therefore, it is challenging for computer systems to solve wicked problems. For instance, say you want to design a residential building, but your client does not know all the exact requirements at the beginning of the project. The requirements may exist, but they can change at any time as the project develops. Or maybe your client wants a "stylish design" – but, given that what comprises an elegant design is open to interpretation, this definition as well could change at any time during the project.

A tame problem is a problem that is well understood and cannot change over time. In these problems, you have a fixed set of equations or rules that are known from the outset, and the solution to these problems is either right or wrong. These problems can be easily defined for computer systems. For instance, in a game like chess or Go, you have a board, a set of game pieces, and you know the rules for each piece. Or, in structural engineering, you can mathematically define how to calculate stress or deflections in beams and columns. By defining the rules of the game or governing formula in the structure, you can run and solve these problems using computer systems.

The point is, if you see that AI can win against humans in the games of chess or Go (a tame problem), you should not generalize that success to their ability to handle wicked problems – especially those in AEC.

Most of the problems that AI solves today are incredibly well-defined and narrowly scoped. This is where the term "narrow AI" comes in. Most of the issues in AEC need more generic solutions, a.k.a. general AI, which are flexible and adaptable to various conditions, and we are many years away from that. All of the comments from AEC experts that I quoted at the beginning of this section refer to "general AI," which won't happen in our lifetime.

The fear of AI taking over, or the illusion that it can do anything, occurs when people see a narrowly scoped solution handling a very tiny tame problem, and think that solution can handle complex, wicked problems under various circumstances.

Now, let's talk about the third misconception: media hype!

Misconception 3: Falling for media hype

Media plays a significant role in creating misconceptions about AI, and I can understand the reasons why. Would you like to watch a movie in which the main character is a car with an autopilot feature that kills the driver by going under a trailer, simply because the AI model was not trained for that situation? Or would you rather watch a movie in which the main character is a far more sophisticated and exciting transformer car? Obviously, the answer is the latter. All media, whether entertainment or news, want to give you some excitement: they are in the business of selling more subscriptions and getting more ad views and clicks, and talking about the limitations of a narrow AI does not yield any of that.

For instance, here is the article on AlphaGo from *Forbes*, written by Parmy Olson in 2016:

Google Makes AI History by Beating World "Go" Champion

Google DeepMind's AlphaGo program has now beaten Go champion Lee Sedol in its second of five matches. The game started at 1:00 pm Seoul, South Korea time on Thursday, March 10 [2016].

In 1952 a computer beat a human at tic-tac-toe. Then in 1994, it trumped another one at checkers. In 1997 IBM's Deep Blue computer beat chess champion, Garry Kasparov, at chess. Today [March 9, 2016] at 1:00 pm local time in Seoul, Korea (around 4:00 am London time), Google's AlphaGo computer took on the legendary Lee Sedol at the ultra-complicated board game known as Go and won after three and a half hours... this is a major breakthrough for artificial intelligence, thanks to the profound complexity of the game Go. [12]

Indeed, this event was a major accomplishment for DeepMind and the AI community. But to set the right expectations for others, I wish that the journalist who wrote this article, and those who write similar types of articles, would include something about the limitations of AlphaGo or other AI agents – some sort of disclaimer, such as:

"AlphaGo only works on Go, a game with predefined and well-known rules. Please do not assume this solution can solve any other real-world problem; it only works on the tame problem of Go."

How to avoid misconceptions

The only way to avoid falling for these misconceptions is to undertake AI education: reading books, newspapers, magazines, and blogs written by credible sources. (If you have a difficult time finding credible sources, head to www.mehdinourbakhsh.com to receive an AI newsletter, book recommendations, and stay up to date with AI.) Now that you know what the origins of AI misunderstanding are, it's time to talk about how to interact with AI systems.

Interaction with AI systems

Interaction with AI systems is about how you act and deal with the AI system and how the AI system works with you. Understanding this interaction is crucial in learning what AI systems are, and how you should build them or assess them when they've been made for you.

Imagine you have three sports cars parked in your garage. On the surface they look identical, but they provide very different driving experiences. The first car has no automation, so you need to do all the driving tasks as a driver. The second car has an AI engine with partial automation: it can accelerate and decelerate, but requires you to monitor the surrounding environment and take the steering wheel. In this case, you and the AI system need to work in harmony to complete the driving task. The third car has a fully autonomous AI system: it can perform all the driving functions, so you don't need to perform any task to get to your destination.

These levels of autonomy are classified into six categories by the SAE J3016 standard in a document entitled "Taxonomy and definitions for terms related to driving automation systems for on-road motor vehicles" [13]. For simplicity, I have compressed these six categories into three groups in Table 5-1.

NO AUTOMATION	PARTIAL AUTOMATION	FULL AUTOMATION
LEVEL 1	LEVEL 2	LEVEL 3
Driver performs all the driving tasks.	The vehicle can perform some tasks, such as acceleration and deceleration. The driver is responsible for monitoring the driving environment and performing the driving tasks in collaboration and with the assistance of the vehicle.	The vehicle performs all the driving tasks and functions. The driver is hands-off.

Table 5-1: Simplified spectrum of autonomy in autonomous cars

Even though all three cars look the same, your interaction with these AI systems makes your driving experience completely different for each car.

When I go to conferences, I often ask people which is their favorite level of autonomy. This is a tricky question, because there is no right or wrong answer. The answer depends on the situation and the environment in which you want to use your car. If you enjoy driving your sports car around California's Napa Valley, you may not want any automation: you just want the experience of driving in such a beautiful place. Conversely, when you get stuck in a traffic jam on the way to the office the next day, you want automation to take over so that you can read your book or check your emails while you crawl along. The level of automation depends on the situation and environment in which the car is used and the level of support you need from the AI system.

Your preferred level of automation in AI systems depends on the situation, the environment, and your need for support from the AI system.

The same applies to problems in the design, planning, and execution of AEC projects. For instance, you may have designed thousands of bathrooms before, and now want automation to take over and design the bathroom for you (Level 3). Or, you may have received a unique commission from a new client who wants you to design the most luxurious bathrooms in the world. In this case, you want to think deeply and create the most imaginative designs of your career, so you may not want any automation at all (Level 1).

Let's consider an example in construction. Inspecting the work-in-place for payment applications in large projects takes time, and it is error-prone. In this situation, having an AI system that can go to the construction site and capture what is done could have a considerable value (Level 3). You will learn about this use case and how the team at Swinerton has done it in the next chapter.

In other use cases you might want to make all the decisions yourself, and just need an AI agent to help you provide quick advice and feedback. For example, say you want to simulate the performance of a hundred building variations you designed, but your project schedule does not allow you to simulate them one by one. AI can help by giving you instant feedback on performance simulation when you design, so that you can make the right decisions (Level 2). Going back to the bathroom design example, it could be the case that you want to design the bathroom on your own, but need advice or feedback from an AI system about building codes and local requirements for the project (Level 2).

Let's put all this together in Table 5-2.

As you can see in Table 5-2, we have three levels of automation: no AI automation (let's call it "Do it myself"), semi-automation ("Do it together"), and full automation ("Do it for me"). Let me explain each of these levels:

1) Do it myself

Task: Some of the tasks you do give you a lot of energy, and you want to do them all by yourself. You are passionate about the work you do, or you are being challenged in a positive way, so you want no automation.

	LEVEL 1 NO AUTOMATION DO IT MYSELF	LEVEL 2 PARTIAL AUTOMATION DO IT TOGETHER	LEVEL 2 FULL AUTOMATION DO IT FOR ME
Interaction	You perform all the tasks.	You and the AI system work together to perform the tasks.	The AI system does the task for you.
Analogy	The AI system does not exist.	The AI system is your advisor and mentor.	The AI system is your employee.
Example	You design the bathroom with no automation.	You design the bathroom while the AI system gives you feedback about local codes, project cost, time, etc.	The AI system designs the bathroom for you.
Decision	You make all the decisions.	The AI system provides relevant information. You make all the decisions.	The AI system makes all the decisions on your behalf.
Solution Explainability	You can explain the solution and the journey to get to the solution.	You can explain the solution and the journey to get to the solution because you made all the decisions that led to the solution.	You may not be able to explain why and how the final solution is created because of important decisions made by the AI system.

Table 5-2: The spectrum of AI autonomy in AEC

Interaction: In this case, you don't need AI.

2) Do it together

Task: Sometimes, the task you do depends on consultants, supervision from subject-matter experts in your company, or analysis from external resources that can take time to get to you. You just need quick feedback to get going, and you wish you could automate that part.

Interaction: In this case, you want to collaborate and work with the AI system in completing a task. The AI system is responsible for giving you quick feedback, like an advisor and mentor, while you are responsible for making the decisions. The harmonious workflow with the AI system is very iterative and involves you taking a small step, getting feedback from the AI system, and moving on to the next step. Once you have completed the task, you can explain to others what decisions you made and how you came up with your best solution, and all the solutions in between.

3) Do it for me

Task: Sometimes, the task you do is time-consuming, repetitive, or drains your energy. Perhaps you have done it a hundred times and you're getting bored doing it again and again, or the task is becoming impossible to do on a tight deadline. So, you prefer to automate it from start to end.

Interaction: In this case, you want to delegate the task to the AI system. You are responsible for telling the AI system what you wish and setting it up for success. The AI system has the autonomy to make decisions on your behalf to deliver what you asked for. In other words, the AI system acts as your employee, and it does what you want it to do. One thing it may not be able to do, however, is explain "how" the job is done and the "why" of the outcome. This might be a problem if you want to explain the AI outputs to others.

When you think about some of the tasks you do every day, what level of AI automation do you need – "do it myself," "do it together," or "do it for me"?

Let's summarize this. The appropriate level of interaction with the AI system depends on the situation in which you want to use it. Even for the same task (e.g., the bathroom design), sometimes you want full automation, sometimes no automation, and sometimes you want to collaborate with your AI system to make more informed decisions.

Knowing which level of automation solves your problem and communicating this to your AI team or technology provider is the key to building an AI system that satisfies your needs. I often hear from designers that AI systems that use evolutionary algorithms and make too many decisions (Level 3) are not desirable for their creative design work. They are right. Perhaps they need quick feedback on several design solutions they created to make better decisions (Level 2). In the next chapter, you will learn how teams at Perkins & Will use Level 2 automation to design high-performing buildings.

When it comes to AI systems and automation, one size doesn't fit all. We all have different problems and different preferences in automating tasks.

Inherent limitations of AI systems* [22]

To demonstrate the inherent limitations of AI systems or what AI systems cannot do, let me share with you the story of a robot and a fake ticking bomb.

A group of scientists were excited to test out their new intelligent robot. The primary job of the robot was to defend itself from a fake ticking bomb placed on a cart in an adjacent room. They had been training the robot for the past several months using various AI techniques. The robot learned that the bomb was powered by a battery, and in order to defuse the bomb it should take the battery out of the room. One of the scientists pushed the start button, and the test got underway. The robot went to the room and saw that the battery was sitting next to the fake bomb on the cart. So, it moved the cart and battery out of the room, and – *BOOM!!!* – the fake bomb went off. The problem? The robot didn't know that moving the cart out of the room also moved the fake bomb that was on the cart.

So in the second attempt, the AI scientists changed their strategy: "before taking any action, the robot should analyze the intended implications of its actions and the implications of all possible side effects." So, the robot went into the room. It deduced that touching the cart would not change the color of the bomb, the battery, the room, or the size of the cart, the door, the walls, the wheels... *BOOM!!!* The fake bomb went off again.

"We must teach the robot to ignore the irrelevant implications," the scientists said. So, they improved the robot by teaching it to find and put irrelevant implications into a list and ignore them. The third test got started; this time, the robot got stuck before entering the room. The scientists yelled, "Do something!" The robot replied, "There are so

---

* This section is inspired by and adapted from Kenneth Cukier, Viktor Mayer-Schön-berger, and Francis de Véricourt's book *Framers: Human Advantage in an Age of Technology and Turmoil.*

many..." *BOOM!!!* There were so many irrelevant implications for the robot to find and process that it couldn't complete this preparatory task before it was too late to do its main task.

This story was inspired by an essay called "Cognitive wheels: The frame problem of AI," published by philosopher and cognitive scientist Daniel Dennett in the mid-1980s [14]. Even though the field of AI has changed significantly since then, the fundamentals of what AI cannot do have not. The robot's three failures demonstrate three things that humans are good at, but AI is not: causation, counterfactuals, and constraints. In the first scenario, the robot failed to see cause and effect. In the second scenario, the robot failed to find relevant counterfactuals, and in the third scenario, it failed because it applied too many constraints to the problem.

In the next section I will discuss what causation, counterfactuals, and constraints are, and how the human brain considers and uses these factors in its thinking and decision-making. I will also discuss the limitations that AI has in each of these areas, and how that limits the scope and reach of its abilities. To create a more relevant discussion, I will focus on the learning-based AI systems, because machine learning, and more specifically deep learning, is the most talked-about AI topic in the mainstream media.

Causation

In the brain

As explained by Kenneth Cukier, Viktor Mayer-Schönberger, and Francis de Véricourt in their book *Framers: Human Advantage in an Age of Technology and Turmoil*, humans use causal templates that help us generate abstractions. For example, if we see that hot charcoal causes painful burns, we can say that a red-hot furnace or volcanic lava can cause painful harm. Through these abstract causal templates, we can explain the world. For instance, you can explain to a child that you get burnt *because* the charcoal is hot, and the heat damages our skin tissues.

Being able to explain things helps us in two ways: learning (when you explain, you learn!) and generalizing. For instance, you can say that all types of heat cause skin burns, no matter what the source is.

Causal templates in our brain help us with abstraction, which we use to explain, learn, and generalize things.

In AI systems

While learning causal relationships and transferring learnings from one domain to another is an active area of research, most of today's mainstream AI systems, which use the machine learning branch of the AI tree, learn by association rather than causation. In other words, they learn by identifying the correlation between the variables. For instance, let's say you have a dataset of chocolate consumption and average income. Given the chocolate consumption per household, your model can predict the income of the household with 99% accuracy, which means your model found a strong correlation between chocolate consumption and household income. Your model shows that more consumption of chocolate correlates with more household income. In this scenario, you may say wealthy people consume more chocolate, but you cannot say chocolate *causes* people to become wealthy. It is not a cause-and-effect relationship.

Let's try another example in construction safety. Say you have a dataset of accidents that includes the weather, the food served in your cafeteria, and the number of accidents for each given day. After training your machine learning model, you'll see that there is a strong relationship between pizza and accidents on site. You may mistakenly conclude that eating pizza "causes" accidents, and even decide to remove it from the menu. But in reality, the number of accidents won't drop. The reason is that your machine learning model only shows the association between these variables (number of accidents and eating pizza), not the causation. What causes your accidents is not presented in your dataset.

Most learning-based AI systems show the degree of association between the input and output variables, not the cause and effect.

Because AI does not understand cause-and-effect relationships, you cannot expect AI systems to have causal templates to abstract observations and generalize them. And without a causal abstraction, every situation is novel – it's as if the situation has not been seen before. For instance, the results of a machine learning model that can predict the cost of *commercial buildings in San Francisco* cannot be generalized to other scenarios, such as predicting the cost of *residential* buildings in San Francisco or commercial buildings in *Los Angeles*. You need to generate a new dataset for these new scenarios and retrain your model.

Besides the ability to generalize, another issue caused by the absence of a cause-and-effect understanding is the lack of explainability. You cannot really explain the results of a solution generated by learning-based AI systems – hence the term, "black box." In Prof. Judea Pearl and Dana Mackenzie's *The Book of Why: The New Science of Cause and Effect*, Pearl, who is known for his fundamental contributions to AI through the development of a calculus for probabilistic and causal reasoning, explains:

> "With Bayesian networks [a graph for representing probabilistic causal relationship], we had taught machines to think in shades of gray, and this was an important step toward humanlike thinking. But we still couldn't teach machines to understand causes and effects. We couldn't explain to a computer why turning the dial

of a barometer won't cause rain... Without the ability to envision alternate realities and contrast them with the currently existing reality, a machine cannot ... answer the most basic question that makes us human: 'Why?'" [15]

Learning-based AI systems cannot explain their solution because they don't understand the cause and effect.

Counterfactuals

In the brain

Counterfactuals are our ability to dream about an alternative reality. They are answers to hypothetical questions like, "What would have happened if...?" They help us to imagine what isn't there and uncover different causes to explain why things happen. For instance, let's say you barbecued some vegetables or meat, and found that the food was uncooked inside but burnt on the outside. You ask yourself, "What would have happened if I cooked the food at a lower temperature? Or used a lower temperature at the start of the cooking process, then a higher temperature at the end?" These are counterfactual questions.

In AI systems

AI systems cannot imagine a new situation or answer counterfactual questions. Since they work based on previously obtained observations and data, they can, by definition, only look backward at what happened in the past. This is one of the major limitations in the application of AI systems, especially in cases where safety is important. In self-driving cars, for example, there are millions of accident scenarios that the car has not seen; this is why you frequently hear on the news about crashes involving self-driving cars. They have not seen enough of that situation before! To create data for possible crashes that have not yet happened, scientists imagine alternative realities and use car simulators to synthetically create rare accident situations; these are known as edge cases. But the incident in which a Tesla Model 3 crashed into an overturned truck on the highway suggests that AI scientists cannot predict all possible edge cases. (So, with that in mind, please use the autopilot function with caution!)

In AEC, for example, let's say you trained an AI system to predict housing price fluctuations so that you can buy property before your competitors and at the right time. This AI system, which uses past data, cannot come up with hypothetical what-if scenarios – e.g., "What would happen if the market cools down in the near future?" – on its own and adjust its price predictions accordingly. Even if the market actually does cool down, your AI system can still only give predictions based on data from the past. This inherent AI limitation caused Zillow to lose $420 million during the pandemic, as their AI system kept "zestimating" high even though the housing market was cooling down, leading them to buy many houses at higher prices than they should have [16].

AI systems cannot imagine new scenarios or answer counterfactual questions because they work with data that is made up of observations in the past.

Constraints

In the brain

Constraints are rules and restrictions that bind our imaginations. They are extremely useful because by changing them, you can shape alternative realities. Without them, your brain gets exhausted from coming up with too many useless scenarios. For example, in the barbecue example, you probably don't imagine unlikely scenarios such as, "What would have happened if a polar bear had taken the meat or vegetables?" Our imaginations are bound by constraints that make them hew closer to reality. This is how we avoid processing too much information when imagining an alternative reality.

We, as humans, solve problems, make decisions, and take actions using causation, counterfactuals, and constraints. This is what AI systems, especially those working with data, cannot do.

In AI systems

While AI systems work within the constraints defined for them, they lack the ability to impose new boundaries and constraints on their own. Because of this limitation, the exploration of solutions often becomes time-consuming and, even worse, we get subpar solutions. For instance, let's say you used 100,000 building models to develop a learning-based AI system that generates building mass. The AI system can indefinitely generate building masses that could be completely irrelevant.

One of the questions that I often hear from business executives is, "Why can AI not give me the best three options instead of creating so many?" The answer is that AI systems that generate lots of solutions cannot constrain them on their own. These constraints should be pre-defined in the AI system, which may result in creating subpar solutions, especially for wicked AEC problems.

It would be a lot better if AI systems could compose new bound conditions to explore the solution space more efficiently, but the fact is, they can't.

Learning-based AI systems cannot impose new constraints and boundary conditions on their own.

Now that you know about the inherent limitations of AI systems and what they cannot do, it's time to talk about their biases.

Biases in AI systems

So far you have learned about how our brain solves problems by considering causation, counterfactuals, and constraints. Thinking takes energy, and to consume less energy, our brain creates shortcuts that favor something or someone, sometimes fairly and sometimes unfairly. This built-in function, known as implicit bias, exists in everyone. In fact, we have more than 180 biases (e.g., gender bias, ageism, affinity bias, confirmation bias, attribution bias, conformity bias) that we should be aware of if we want to create a diverse, inclusive, and equitable environment that we can all live in.

These biases affect every decision we make and everything we do. That's why our AI systems also have biases – because we make them! When you use an AI system, you are either making critical decisions based on the feedback you receive from the AI system (Level 2), or letting the AI system make decisions on your behalf (Level 3). But what if you realize one day that these AI systems are biased towards a certain answer or solution, and thus caused you to make a wrong decision?

This is what happened to Amazon. The company receives hundreds of thousands of résumés every day, and the recruiters would be overwhelmed if they had to review all of them. Therefore, the company decided to use an AI system to review job candidates and tell the recruiters which candidates were fit for the job. After using and testing the model for a while, they realized that the machine learning model had a bias towards recruiting men, and ranked women lower [17]. They found the problem and fixed it, but there's a lesson to learn here.

The best way to minimize AI systems' biases is to know where they come from. The answer? They come from us, because we build the AI system.

Let's take a closer look at some of the ways we can create biases in AI systems.

- **Problem formulation:** one of the roles of the AI engineer or scientist is to convert a wicked problem into a tame problem. They interpret and make lots of assumptions to convert the problem into something that computers can execute.
- **Data preparation:** as we covered in Chapter 4, your data can be sensory data, human-created data, or synthetic data. Each of these data categories is subject to human biases. For instance, the location and angle of your camera (sensory data), the distribution of data from your past projects and the labeling of your data (human-created data), or the assumptions made in creating the algorithm that synthesized your dataset (synthetic data) could lead to developing AI solutions with inherent bias.
- **Algorithm and parameter selection:** to create a solution, AI engineers or scientists need to choose an AI algorithm and tune their parameters to accurately do the task or make a recommendation. The choice of algorithms and how we tune them plays a major role in creating biases in AI systems.

Knowing how biases are created in an AI system can help you mitigate them when running your project. But how? The answer is diversity, inclusion, and equity.

- **Diversity:** you need to create a diverse AI team and promote a culture in which different perspectives are encouraged. Having people on your team with different cultures, races, genders, sexual orientations, and even technical backgrounds can help you mitigate the unconscious bias that one person may have in formulating the problem and creating the AI solution. You can find out more about how to create a diverse AI team in Chapter 7.
- **Inclusion:** you need to examine how representative of the entire population your data is. In the case of Amazon, their dataset consisted of about 60% men and 40% women, so the trained model leaned towards men because they were more represented in the dataset. To take an example from the AEC space, when you're building bridges you have a dataset of all bridges you have built in the past. Assuming that 70% of these past bridges were made of reinforced concrete, the AI solution will probably propose a reinforced concrete bridge when predicting the most suitable bridge for a given terrain.
- **Equity:** how fair are the results of the AI system when you examine it? This is where you need to create systematic test cases that represent your entire population. For instance, you can catch the bias in the Amazon example when you prepare résumés of the people you'd hire from different ages, genders, and sexual orientation to test it out against the algorithm's results. The explainability of the solutions that AI suggests is crucial. As discussed earlier, explainability is one of the limitations of machine learning. That's why researchers have been looking more into this important topic in recent years.

AI systems have biases because humans make them. Knowing about these biases can help you mitigate them, which you can do either by forming a diverse AI team or by asking the right questions and testing the AI solution developed for you.

Let's put it all together

Our brain is wired to use causal abstractions to explain, generalize, and learn things that happen in the world. When you see a success story in the media about an AI solution to a tame problem, you generalize it to all sorts of problems and may try to connect it to some of our wicked problems in AEC. But that connection is not there.

For an AI system to work, a human (i.e., an AI engineer or scientist) needs to convert a wicked problem into a tame problem that can be solved by AI. In this process, the scientist needs to think about causation in order to extract relevant variables, counterfactuals in order to anticipate all the different scenarios that the AI system may or may not work with, and constraints in order to define boundaries around the problem.

In this scenario, the AI system is like a puppet, and the human who created it is like the puppet master. The media depiction of AI is of a puppet without strings, which creates unrealistic excitement or fear about AI.

I hope that what we discussed in this chapter didn't discourage you, but rather gave you a realistic point of view about AI. AI is an extremely powerful and underutilized technology in AEC. Given the narrow AI we have today, the best strategy for developing AI systems in complex AEC projects is building a symbiotic relationship between humans and AI.

As humans, we are good at ideation, creative thinking, working in fuzzy environments, and solving extremely complex AEC problems. Computers, especially with cloud computing, are good at processing and analyzing lots and lots of data to solve narrow and tame problems faster, more cheaply, and more efficiently than a human. What if we could put the best of both worlds together?

With the three levels of automation, you learned that AI can take care of the tame problems and/or the mundane tasks that you don't want to do so that you can focus on the more creative and less tedious parts of your job.

Synergy and collaboration between humans and AI are what we should aim for, because AI alone is not going to solve our wicked AEC problems.

KEY TAKEAWAYS

- There is a big gap between what AI can really do and what it is depicted as being capable of doing in the media.
- We tend to overestimate what an AI system can do because we, as humans, are good at abstracting observations and ideas.
- "Do it myself," "do it together," and "do it for me" are the three levels of AI automation.
- In "do it together," you and the AI system work in collaboration – you are responsible for making decisions based on the feedback and advice you receive from the AI.
- In "do it for me," you define what you want to delegate and leave the decision-making to the AI system.
- The level of AI automation that you need depends on the situation, the environment, and the energy that doing the task gives or takes from you.
- The conversion of wicked problems to tame problems is critical in defining AI systems. You should be aware of all the assumptions made in this process.
- Causal templates in our brain help us with abstraction, which we use to explain, learn, and generalize things. Most mainstream learning-based AI systems can identify the association between inputs and outputs, but not the causation.
- Learning-based AI systems cannot create counterfactual scenarios – it is the job of the AI engineer to predict all the counterfactuals and create data. Failure to do so may result in devastating results.

KNOW WHAT AI SYSTEMS ARE

- Learning-based AI systems cannot create new boundary conditions. They only work in the predefined boundary condition that they are designed for.
- Synergy and collaboration between humans and AI are what we should aim for, because AI alone will not solve our complex AEC problems.

A PROBLEM SHARED

Shane Burger is a principal and internationally recognized leader at Woods Bagot. He directs a division centered on technical innovation, and leads a global team dedicated to researching, developing, and applying new design and delivery models to projects. I asked Shane how he sees the role of the search and optimization branch of AI in design, and what AI really can or cannot do. He responded as follows:

There's a gap between what AI, especially the search and optimization branch, can really do and how it is being marketed in the AEC industry. Some companies promise architects that optimization and AI will revolutionize their workflows to the point where some think their job won't exist ten years from now.

This is not true.

AI is good at solving well-defined or structured problems. For instance, structural analysis, daylighting, and acoustics are very well-defined problems because you have a well-constrained problem with fixed parameters. You know the direct relationship between the inputs and outputs and how to compute them.

What AI is not good at are problems that are not well-defined and are highly dependent on the designer's interpretations – for instance, designing an elegant space or unique form. These problems are vague and not well understood by computer systems. In other words, these problems are not quantifiable or measurable, making AI less suitable to work with.

Another limitation of AI solutions is that you often must define parametric topologies with a predefined range of rooms or furniture, or particular arrangements of objects. In other words, you define your entire geometry system from the outset at the beginning of the project and cannot expect AI to create something outside of those parameters. Or, if you want to use it in another project, you probably need to redefine your geometry system.

So this is where I start running into questions of credibility when it comes to these soft design practices where human experience and intuition are precious. It's where we, as designers, come into play.

I'm a healthy skeptic when it comes to the use of AI in design. When I see an example of using AI in soft and subjective design problems, such as space planning, I start thinking and asking questions about how the problem is formulated for the computer system. 'How did you define the connectivity between people?' or 'How did you consider the biological and sociological aspects of people working together?'

My advice to other leaders and executives is to familiarize yourself with what AI can or cannot really do so that you can ask the right question when technologists present it to you.

CHAPTER 6

Explore AI systems in AEC

My dog, Goofy, is a Havanese terrier mix. In his world, every person has the potential to give him a treat, so he loves people. He is very outgoing, likes nature, and loves to chase squirrels and cats. He is a couch potato, and he barely barks. But despite his cool, calm nature, he gets defensive when he sees things he has not seen before and cannot understand.

Once my wife and I took Goofy to a national park full of big redwood trees. We chose a picnic table, spread out our lunch, and tied Goofy's leash firmly to the table. Goofy was cool, calm, and content, as usual. While we were having lunch, fifteen or twenty people gathered for a gender reveal celebration about twenty yards from our table. They had lots of balloons, colorful signs and decorations, and started playing loud music. It was a party!

Then, all of a sudden, the gender reveal surprise box arrived. It was a huge box – about three feet long and three feet wide – wrapped in bright, shiny silver and gold paper. The man carrying the box held it on his shoulder, and from our angle we could not see his head; it was as if a shiny box with a body and two legs was walking across the ground in front of us.

For Goofy, the scene looked bizarre – he must have thought an alien was parading in front of him. So, naturally, he went crazy and started barking non-stop, as if he was under attack. He tried to rush towards the person carrying the huge box, but his leash was tied to the table. He was furious! Later, when the person carrying the box put it down, the alien became human in Goofy's eyes, and he immediately stopped barking.

Whenever Goofy sees new sights and doesn't comprehend what they are, his fight-or-flight response gets triggered and he goes crazy. As humans, we also have a built-in fight-or-flight response in our brain. In their article "What happens in the brain when we feel fear?" Dr. Arash Javanbakht and Dr. Linda Saab, professors of psychiatry from Wayne State University, say:

> "Threat stimulus, such as the sight of a predator, triggers a fear response in the amygdala, which activates areas involved in preparation for motor functions involved in fight or flight. It also triggers release of stress hormones and sympathetic nervous system." [18]

While the response to fear has served humanity well for millions of years, it also has some downsides in the era of modern technology. When we fear something like technology or artificial intelligence, our fight-or-flight mode is triggered and we can start talking about it or acting against it without giving it actual consideration.

Acting in fight-or-flight mode removes the curiosity you need to learn about the technology, especially AI systems.

Dr. John Haymaker, director of research at Perkins & Will, explains how we can remove the non-rational fear of AI:

> "If you don't understand what AI systems are, then there is a risk of developing non-rational fear about them. As a result, you won't

be able to identify their benefits. You should be curious about AI systems and get to know them. This is the only way we can remove the non-rational fear that exists in some parts of our industry."

One of the reasons we are afraid of something in a specific situation is because we don't have control. Let me explain. Imagine you are in a desert, twenty feet away from a starving lion. The lion is looking at you, and you have nowhere to go. This is the time when your fight-or-flight response will kick in. Now imagine the same hungry lion twenty feet away, but this time in a zoo where you have a fence between you. This time, instead of being afraid, you are curious and want to learn more about the lion. Why? Because you have control over the situation.

When it comes to AI systems, you have control, and you have choices to make. You can choose to ignore AI and let the technologists build whatever they think is suitable for you. Or, you can be curious and educate yourself about AI systems, such that you can lead and direct your team or the technology providers to create the right technology for our industry.

But how can you learn about AI systems in AEC? In my opinion, the best way to learn about AI systems is to see them in action. In this chapter, we'll review three AI systems and projects in the design, prefabrication, and construction domains. In the first project, the AI algorithm learns how to simulate the building energy performance. Once learned, it can perform building simulations in a fraction of a second, enabling architects to design better buildings. In the second project, an AI recommendation system helps architects propose the right prefabrication components at the early design phase. And in the last project, the AI agent allows contractors and owners to inspect work-in-place for payment applications.

These are real AI projects that are either completed or in the development phase. Because of confidentiality, we are not going to discuss the biases in these AI systems.

AI Agent 1: Learning to simulate

Dr. John Haymaker is the director of research at Perkins & Will, a global design practice founded in 1935. I shared with you his point of view about the role of AI in design at the end of Chapter 3. John is very passionate about creating design systems that enhance decision-making. His research team at Perkins & Will led and developed several AI systems in space planning, decision-making, and surrogate modeling, which is a class of AI systems that predict simulation results (in this example, building energy performance). This is what John had to say about his project:

"In the schematic design phase of projects, we often have two weeks to create design options and recommendations for our clients. To come up with those design options, we create several different building design alternatives and evaluate them against the project's performance requirements, such as energy and daylighting. Our goal is to find the best design parameters (e.g., building orientation, windows width, roof overhang, and materials of exterior walls) to minimize the energy use of buildings.

"In a typical process, we pass these parameters, along with other building parameters, to Energy Plus and Radiance for energy and daylighting simulations. These simulation engines, on average, take twenty to thirty minutes to return the energy consumption and the daylight performance of buildings. This twenty-to-thirty-minute simulation time is the major bottleneck in our projects. Let me explain why.

"We are a dedicated R&D team that helps the designers of the company make better decisions. In the schematic design phase, they make important decisions about the building orientation, façade, core, and so on. Typically, they send us the latest design decisions they want to make and walk us through the design parameters they have. For instance, we want to design a façade that is fixed in four corners, but we can change the curvature at the center within a specific range. We take this information to create various design alternatives quickly. The challenge is that we only have a twenty-four-hour turnaround because the entire schematic design process is fourteen days, and they need to make decisions on other parts of the design.

"Even though we can create thousands of solutions, we only have the time to run energy and daylighting simulations on sixty of them during the twenty-four-hour time limit. Since these calculations take a lot of time, we rely on best practices and intuition rather than systematic design explorations. That's why the simulation time becomes a bottleneck in creating better design solutions.

"We need to reduce the time of simulation to explore more and find high-performing building solutions. Otherwise, our buildings will produce more carbon, consume more energy, and have poor lighting conditions, which brings in negative impacts to the health and well-being of occupants.

"To summarize, our two challenges were the short time frame of the schematic design phase, and the computational demands of exploring a more extensive solution space. So, we need to find a way to rapidly explore many design possibilities. Even though parametric and generative designs exist, they take a long time to set up the problem, and they don't necessarily reduce the simulation *time. Introduced by Victor Okhoya and his PhD work at Carnegie Mellon University, we realized that AI was an answer because it could help us significantly reduce the time of the simulation.*

"AI could help us replace energy simulation with prediction. So, instead of using a simulation engine to calculate the energy performance of buildings, we used a prediction engine that could estimate the simulation results in milliseconds. To train our machine learning model, we created a synthetic dataset of 1,000 buildings. Then we fed these buildings into the Energy Plus simulator and stored the data in a database. We used this data to train a machine learning model that could predict the buildings' energy, daylighting, and carbon dioxide emissions. One of the limitations of the model is that it is not generalizable to all building types, and should be retrained accordingly.

"Using this prediction engine, we can instantly predict a building's energy and daylighting performance instead of waiting for thirty minutes. This means we can design better buildings. We don't use AI to generate more buildings quickly: we use it to formulate better design questions in the projects and ultimately design high-quality and performative buildings.

"At Perkins & Will, we have moved away from using evolutionary algorithms (EAs) and use learning-based AI algorithms instead. The problem with the EAs is that they make many decisions on our behalf [Level 3]. So, when we receive the optimum design as an answer, we cannot trust it – because ultimately, design is a decision-making process. We need AI to help us understand and navigate the space of alternative solutions by analyzing the space and providing feedback and insights, rather than receiving the best design without even knowing the solution space the algorithm has

been through. We are moving towards learning-based algorithms
because we prefer to have guidance and quick feedback from AI to
make our own design decisions [Level 2] rather than having the
decision made on our behalf by EAs [Level 3]."

Before sharing the next example, let's review the problem described
above and see how it's related to what we have discussed so far.

In terms of the 3Ps (pressure, productivity, profitability), it is clear
that John's team is under *pressure* to design better in a very short time.
They can potentially increase their *profit* by increasing the quality and
performance of their designs and saving energy for their happy and
returning clients. To do that, they need to design and simulate thousands of buildings, but they only have twenty-four hours to get back to
their designers. Their *productivity* is hindered by how time-consuming
simulation engines are. Their simulation takes time because they perform highly accurate mathematical operations. However, that level of
accuracy may not be needed at that early stage of design, when there is
still lots of uncertainty. Therefore, we can replace these time-consuming
simulators with real-time machine learning models that might be less
accurate, but good enough for the early design phase.

How does a surrogate model work?

To use any simulator, you have a set of inputs (e.g., building orientation, windows width, roof orientation). The simulator takes in these
parameters as an input, runs various mathematical operations (let's call
it the mathematical function), and generates outputs (e.g., a building's
energy consumption). Every time you run a simulator, the mathematical function converts the inputs to the outputs. If you can provide
enough examples of inputs and outputs, the machine learning model
can learn the mapping between them. In other words, it learns the
mathematical function that connects the input to the output. Once
learned, you can use the machine learning model to predict the output,

given a set of inputs. But this time, the model can predict the results in milliseconds!

What is the AI branch used?

Among all branches, learning-based methods are more suitable for this type of problem. To be more specific, supervised machine learning is used in this type of problem. As you learned in Chapter 3, it is called "supervised" because you need to provide a dataset that has pairs of inputs and outputs of the simulator.

How is data used (5 Vs)?

1. **Volume (scale of data):** there was data from 1,000 buildings in this example.
2. **Velocity (speed of data generation):** each data sample can be generated in twenty to thirty minutes.
3. **Variety (forms of data):** this type of dataset is under the category of computer-generated or synthetic datasets. Typically, researchers run automated scripts that instruct the simulator to generate data.
4. **Veracity (quality of data):** typically, the quality of synthetic data depends on the diversity and similarity to the real-world buildings that the AI system will be used for.
5. **Value of data:** the team captured data aligned with their innovation strategy in their core competency area – designing high-performing buildings.

What are the limitations?

Because of lack of causation, one of the limitations of machine learning models is generalizability. The model only performs well on the data that is used to train it. For instance, if the training set was created using rectangular-shaped buildings of four to ten stories in a certain climate zone and with a maximum length and width of 100 meters, it can only work for buildings within these parameters. Outside of these parameters, the model will not work well. One important job of the AI engineer is finding the right scope for the project: too narrow a scope requires constant retraining (which negates the time-saving), while too diverse a scope (e.g., various building types, dimensions, number of stories, locations) commonly leads to poor and inaccurate results.

What is the desired level of AI automation?

The desired level of automation in this case is Level 2. The AI system can provide quick feedback about the energy performance of buildings while the design decisions are made by the architects.

AI Agent 2: A prefab recommendation engine

Benjamin Callam is the innovation lead at McCarthy, one of the oldest construction companies in the US. He has a background in computer science and computational design, and is experienced in designing and building green and modular housing and offices around the world. Currently, he is leading a group of innovators at McCarthy to investigate how to bring downstream information into the upstream design with offsite construction, especially at the early stage of projects. He believes that the interface between workers or craftsmanship and how our digital business operates has been neglected in our industry for a long time. So, his team is focusing on restitching these two worlds together.

Below, Benjamin describes the AI project that he and his team are working on:

"At McCarthy, we perform and complete more than a hundred proj-ects a year. Each project is like a container that has lots of novel inventions and solutions to difficult problems. However, transfer-ring knowledge from those projects into the larger organization

and reintegrating it into future projects is a big challenge. That's why my team is working on changing this paradigm in the pre-fabrication domain.

"*The challenge with the way we design today is the disconnection between the design and construction of projects. When the project team forms, the designers often make design decisions without prefabrication or construction in mind. Suppose we don't consider the prefabrication products at the early design phase and wait too long. Those products may not be an opportunity anymore because of the long lead time in fabrication, which might be against the project's schedule.*

"*The idea behind our project is to supply designers, as early as possible, with the relevant prefabrication product recommendation so they can make the right decision in serving our clients. In other words, we want to give them the right information at the right time to make go/no-go decisions for prefab components.*

"Our ultimate goal *is to help designers eliminate all unknowns to formulate a complete design at the time of permit. Prefabrication is very time-sensitive because of the multitude of constraints in the decision-making process across multiple stakeholders.*

"*We conceptualize an AI solution to help us improve the deci-sion-making and the current process. We have not built it yet, but we are preparing our data in a format that is readily consumed by the AI agent. Let's say I want to do a project in downtown Phoenix, and we are at the programming stage of the design. This AI recom-mendation engine can help us narrow the potential products and strategies available for use on this project. As the entire company uses this over many projects over time, the AI agent can use our*

*added notes, reviews, and ratings for each strategy to recommend
or not recommend products. It can also provide cost and schedule
estimation based on the product we choose.*

*"The AI recommendation system can have a huge impact on our
design and construction process. Such a tool will not only help
us make decisions faster, to allow us to work on more important
aspects of our job, but also help us reshape the process altogether.*

*"With this new workflow, we can take the learnings from one proj-
ect and apply them seamlessly to another, and escape the project
bubble and approach projects at the portfolio level."*

Let's review the problem that Benjamin's company faced and see
how it is related to what we have discussed so far.

Regarding the 3Ps (pressure, productivity, profitability), I'd say that
the design team is under *pressure* to make go or no-go decisions about
the prefabricated components at the early design stage. It might be
beyond their capabilities to go over all products available in the market
during the short time that they have for design.

Because of the number of choices they have now, and the increased
number of choices in the future, it is counter-*productive* to explore them
manually. And if they don't make the right design decision promptly,
the cost and schedule gain they may get in the project will be missed,
increasing the risk and reducing the *profit*.

This AI agent is a recommendation system (like Netflix or Amazon)
that suggests prefab building products. Imagine having to browse
millions of catalogs of movies on Netflix without a recommendation
Engine: you would spend much of your movie-watching time browsing
to find one worth watching and less time watching what you like. Just
as Netflix recommends a handful of movies to you, Ben's team can
review a shortlist of recommended products, chosen from thousands

of products in their dataset. This way, they can quickly make early design decisions that reduce project schedule, cost, and risk, while increasing the profit margin.

How does an AI recommendation system work?

A recommendation engine suggests relevant products, services, or information. It tries to find the connection between what you need in your project and the available products. What you need in a given project could be elicited from the requirements and/or the patterns of your choices in the previous projects.

What is the AI branch used?

A recommendation engine can use various branches of AI. For instance, you can use machine learning to find the patterns of use in the previous project. Or, if you have some rules that you want the recommendation engine to consider, you can use the knowledge representation and reasoning branch – i.e., a rules-based recommendation engine. The rules-based recommendation engine works well in projects where all the rules are known and identified from the outset.

How is data used (5 Vs)?

1. **Volume (scale of data):** the size of data depends on the catalog of prefab products. If 3D models are stored with fabrication details (LOD 400), the size of the dataset could be significant.
2. **Velocity (speed of data generation):** the speed of data generation depends on the availability of prefabrication components in the market. Over time, you can add them to enhance the dataset.
3. **Variety (forms of data):** having BIM models is ideal for the catalog of prefab components because you can have all the information in one place. However, the file should be accessible and readable by the AI engine. There are also some textual data or

metadata that captures ratings, comments, and other information about the product.

4. **Veracity (quality of data)**: there might be some inconsistencies in data if different people or companies generate the 3D models. Some may have fewer details, or some may have more. There might be some missing information for some products. So, the quality of data becomes a critical component of such a project.

5. **Value of data**: teams at McCarthy have been working with prefab components for a long time. By capturing and leveraging this data, they bring tons of benefits to their construction practice (e.g., centralizing lessons learned) and clients (e.g., lower risk).

What are the limitations?

As mentioned, the recommendation systems try to map two different worlds together: preference in a project or a user, and a catalog of products. You need to supply the products to the recommendation system and define what attributes those products have. So, the AI agent cannot go on the internet and find all the prefab products independently: you need to capture and organize those in a way that is easily consumed by the AI agent. For example, Netflix used to hire many people to watch movies and identify certain characteristics: the movie's genre, who the protagonist is, whether there's a cliffhanger and when it happens, whether the movie has a happy ending, and a lot more. Don't expect the AI agent to work without having a well-structured and organized dataset.

What is the desired level of AI automation?

The desired level of automation in this case is Level 2. The AI system can recommend the matching prefab components, but ultimately designers are responsible for taking the suggestion or not.

AI Agent 3: Boston Dynamic's Spot

Eric Law is a senior director of innovation at Swinerton. He leads an R&D group that aims to change construction by improving schedule, cost, quality, and site safety.

Here is the problem that Eric's team solved with an AI agent, as he describes it:

> *"Like other companies in the industry, we face several problems for tracking and monitoring what has been installed on the job site. Typically, our work-in-place inspection starts on Friday afternoon, when most of the workers leave the job site. Our project engineers, project managers, or superintendents walk the site to count and report what has been done. The problem with the current process is that when three different groups (i.e., general contractors, trade contractors, and owners' representatives) inspect the same 200,000-square-foot building to quantify the work done, they all come back with different numbers, and then they need to discuss and negotiate what number they should use for the progress payment. This is a significant problem, considering we need to do this every month across a hundred different projects. It is a painful and expensive process, subject to human biases and data quality problems. We asked ourselves what would happen if we could capture this data automatically with the help of AI.*

> *"We wanted to develop an AI system to automatically generate quantities for the payment application and check the quality of work-in-place. To do that, I led a team of researchers to run various tests and experimentations with Boston Dynamic. This leading robotics company offers a robotics platform and a mobile robot for construction called Spot.*

"After extensive research, we decided to put a LiDAR scanner, 360-degree cameras, and air monitoring sensors on Spot. LiDAR [light detection and ranging] is a technology for measuring how far away a point on a surface is by calculating the time a laser takes to travel to that point on the object and come back. This technology is often called 3D laser scanning, because it uses the laser to create 3D point clouds.

"After a few experimental runs in the evening, when the job site was quiet, we learned what the robot could do, the risks, and how the people on the site react to it. Often, workers asked for permission to take a photo with Spot, and they had a very positive attitude towards it.

"We piloted Spot and worked on our new way of capturing as-built data for six months. In this new process, we scanned the data in the afternoon and sent the point data and photos to a technology partner. Our partner compared the data with the BIM model of the project and reported back the quantity and the quality of work. Their reports consisted of what's installed in the wrong place, what's missing, and the quantity of work installed from the previous scan. We used this report to update their construction schedule.

"The impact of this AI technology on construction was huge. Imagine a day when the last person on the job site can activate Spot by pushing a button. The robot goes and walks the job site through scanning and, by the next morning, you have your quantity and quality report from the previous day's activities. This could be a big win for the construction industry, considering all the difficulty caused by scheduling updates, inspection, and quantification of work-in-place for the payment application.

"We've got a little bit of work to get there. But we will get there."

Before concluding this chapter, I'd like to review Swinerton's challenge with you so that you can see its relevance to the previous discussions in the book. Let's review the problem.

Regarding the 3Ps (pressure, productivity, profitability), there is a lot of *pressure* on people who want to wrap up their work on a Friday night and go home to their families. They have to walk the site to manually count the work-in-place every week, and then they must negotiate once a month to decide how to calculate progress payments. The entire process is counter-*productive*, time-consuming, error-prone, and uses lots of man hours, which means increases in operation cost, losses, and a lower *profit* margin due to miscalculation. AI is a great solution because it can reduce errors and automate the whole process.

Now, let's talk about Spot and see how it works.

How does Spot work?

Spot is a physical AI agent (a mobile robot), which, by definition, perceives the environment using various sensors, uses AI techniques to analyze the data, and uses its actuators or robotic legs to take actions.

What is the AI branch used?

Going back to the AI tree, you can see that robotics, computer vision, and machine learning are the main branches that Spot uses. Spot can use other branches such as search and/or optimization to find an optimum route or battery usage. As you can see, sometimes multiple branches of the AI tree need to work together to achieve more ambitious automation goals in AEC.

Before talking about data, I should remind you that Spot was used as a carrier of sensory equipment (i.e., a LiDAR scanner, 360-degree cameras, and air monitoring sensors) that Eric's team used to capture as-built data. Let's focus on the as-built data in the next section.

How is data used (5 Vs)?

1. **Volume (scale of data):** depending on the resolution of the scanner and the size of the building, the volume of data could be small or large. In this project, because of the size of the site, the amount of data generated was so large that it became difficult to manage, especially when sending it to the external technology partner. As discussed in Chapter 4, counter to the common belief, sometimes more data is *not* better.

2. **Velocity (speed of data generation):** for the inspection, the data needs to be captured in real time and streamed to a local or remote storage device. The processing of the data, however, can be performed later.

3. **Variety (forms of data):** photos, 3D point clouds, and temperature measures are three forms of data captured.

4. **Veracity (quality of data):** poor-quality scanning for inspection may be caused by the lack of overlap between the scans or the calibration of the scanning device. The quality of scanning also could depend on the weather (if outside) or type of surface (reflective or not) that the laser is being shot at.

5. **Value of data:** the value of the data captured is not just limited to the value that it brings to automating inspection tasks. Collecting as-built data over time and mapping it to the data from building models can help designers and construction companies to close the gap between as-planned and as-built.

What are the limitations?

One of the limitations of this solution was the upload of data and some of the semi-automated processes that the technology partner had to do to compare the as-built to the building models. With improvement in technology in the future, the Swinerton team envisions that creation of BIM from scanned data, and comparing it to the project schedule, could be fully automated.

What is the desired level of AI automation?

The desired level of automation in this case is Level 3. The AI system can navigate the entire construction site and come back with an accurate report on the quantities installed on the site. Unfortunately, the technological limitations meant that the project team could not fully automate the process to meet that goal.

KEY TAKEAWAYS

- The fear of AI causes fight-or-flight reactions, which are detrimental to learning what AI systems are.
- AI in AEC systems helps reduce pressure, increase productivity, and enhance the profit margin of companies.
- The desired level of AI automation depends on the task.

AI REVOLUTION

When I was young, I had two mentors that I used to call uncles. They graduated from the same architecture school in the early 1980s, worked for a few years as architects, and then started their own design and drafting companies.

One uncle had a business strategy that had proven to work for many years: he charged on an hourly basis, and believed that the only way to grow a company was to hire more drafters and get more projects. On the basis of this strategy, he kept getting more projects, hiring more people, and opening more branches. His business was booming at that time.

Meanwhile, at that same time my other uncle had only a handful of employees. He was an out-of-the-box thinker who did not like to follow the convention, and his strategy was different. At first he invested in contemporary technologies and tools like newly developed ruling pens, tracing papers, or T-squares. These evolutionary tools could slightly improve the design outcome, but were not able to get him what he wanted to get out of his investment: market differentiation. In the late '80s, he heard about a revolutionary new technology called CAD, and, to test it out, he made a small bet: he sent out one of his staff to learn and bring CAD to his company. A few months later, he saw that he could deliver high-quality designs faster and better with CAD. So his small bet paid off, and he was all in.

He soon realized that instead of charging on an hourly basis, he could charge based on the value he brought to his clients: fast and high-quality work at 30% below the average price. With his new pricing model, he attracted many new clients. Surprisingly, other drafting companies subcontracted their projects to his company, because he could do the work faster and cheaper than they could themselves. By investing in the revolutionary new technology of CAD, he changed his business model and core competency in the market. None of these were evident at the outset when he started his journey.

This is the story of my two uncles, one visionary, and one conservative. The conservative uncle thought investing in technologies like CAD was ridiculous, because he could not see any benefits it would bring beyond those of his current business model. But even though his business had been thriving at one point, it started to become irrelevant, and he eventually had to declare bankruptcy. The visionary uncle saw a technology opportunity, invested a bit by having an employee train in that technology, and eventually transformed his business model based on what he learned during his transition journey.

Why am I sharing this story, you may ask? Because just like CAD was a revolutionary technology for the drafting business back then, AI is a revolutionary technology to your business today – and as such, it has a huge potential to set you apart from your market competition if you utilize and leverage it to its full potential.

When you employ AI in design or construction, you can design and build faster, cheaper, and better. This way, you can change the processes and products you make, increase your capacity, improve your core competency, and change your business model. In other words, to get the total benefits out of your AI investment, you should optimize your designs, workflows, and even your business model to accommodate it. In the words of Niels W. Falk, CEO and head of consulting and innovation at HD Lab, a Denmark-based technology company:

In the AEC industry, we don't have the notion of optimizing our designs or workflows or even our business models for AI; if we do that, we can get the full benefits of using AI and bring its full potential to our industry.

But these AI benefits, like a massive iceberg with a small visible tip, may not be apparent or detectable from the outset. To see what's below the surface, you should run an AI experimentation project with a fresh and curious mindset. Gilles Caussade, CEO of ConXtech, a US-based fabrication and construction technology company, says:

"AI is a generic technology that can make impossible things possible. But we are not wired to think about the impossible. That's why you need to reset your thinking and expectations when running your first AI project."

You can use AI to create both an intelligent windshield, and an autonomous car: the former is an evolution of a part, and the latter is a revolution in mobility. The choice to run an AI project with an open mind and see AI's full potential in your business is yours – and if you take it, it's one that will allow you to steadily pull away from your competition, even if it looks like your business is thriving without it at the moment.

PART 3

AI in Action

So far in this book, you have learned about AI and some of the AI systems that can and are being used in AEC. But knowing what something is and knowing how to do it are very different things. That's why, in this part of the book, you'll learn about how to run an AI project. Executing an AI project adds another dimension to your AI learning, which is the key to creating a successful AI strategy and adding significant value to your company.

Coming up, you will learn what an AI augmentation framework is. Using this framework, you can start your AI journey by finding the AI use case that best aligns with your business strategy. To do that, you need to work with a team to develop lots of ideas, and then prioritize them based on business viability and technical feasibility. Once that use case is found, you need to work with your internal execution team or find an external AI partner to build a solution the right way. You onboard your team, create conceptual solutions, proofs-of-concept, and a prototype, and test it to improve. Once you have a working prototype that generates acceptable solutions, you need to take it to the piloting phase and go through the cycle of testing it in real-world projects, improving it, and measuring its business viability and how it satisfies various project requirements. Once mature, you can scale and roll out your AI solution in your company.

This part of the book also empowers you with the knowledge that you need to execute your company's first AI project. You can take the learnings from this experimentation and apply them to other projects or create an AI strategy for your company.

People often ask, "Shouldn't you have a strategy in place *before* you run your AI project?" In my experience, whatever you put in place as your strategy before running your first project will change significantly as the project develops. It's better to experiment first, and then define your strategy.

That's why, in Chapter 9, you'll learn how to define an AI strategy. You will start with defining your vision and your "why." Then, you will define various objectives and expected outcomes. Lastly, you will define AI initiatives, which consist of one or a few AI projects. By the end of this chapter, you'll be able to define an AI strategy that empowers you to align all AI efforts in your company.

Ready?

Let's go.

CHAPTER 7

Find the right AI use case

Magda, who used to be the CFO of a manufacturing company, recently accepted an offer to become the CFO of a design company. She had been in her new position for two months, and was getting ready for the annual strategic planning that would happen the following week. As part of her onboarding process, she hired an external strategic consultant to analyze the market, see where they were, and recommend a set of actions. She invited James, the CEO of the company, who had more than thirty-five years of experience in the AEC industry, to the consultant's final presentation.

"Your profit margin is getting smaller. Based on the trends in the market, we anticipate that it will go below 2% in five to seven years," the consultant told them. "We see two main reasons for that. First, projects are getting complex, and you need more resources to design them while keeping the bid price low to win the project. So, your operating cost is going up, which eats up your low margin."

"We've had low margins as long as I can remember. This is not new," said James.

Magda asked, "How do our competitors deal with this?"

"You have two types of competitors," the consultant replied. "The incumbents are other design firms that are innovating and using technology to drive efficiency. Therefore, they can keep their profit margin constant while bidding low. The insurgents are the general contracting firms that added design firms to their portfolio. Since they are in close contact with owners, they convince them to do the design in a shorter time, at a lower cost, and with better coordination. Therefore, they win design projects that you used to win."

The consultant continued, "Your low profit margin brings another major issue to your company. You cannot hire top talent because you cannot afford them, especially the talented data scientists that your company needs."

Magda looked at the consultant and said, "This is very shocking to me. It seems that we are under attack, and we should do something. I'm curious to hear your recommendation."

"Our recommendation is this," the consultant replied. "We recommend you take the defense strategy. It would be best to focus on reducing your operating costs by 30% in the next three years. To do that, you need to increase the maturity of your company by investing in innovation and technology. With this, you can increase the productivity of your designers and the efficiency of your sales, your marketing, and the back end of your business."

James started to laugh. "You're kidding, right? You know that, like lawyers, we charge on an hourly basis. Investing in technology means that we'll be able do things faster, but that will reduce our billable hours and decrease our revenue."

"Yes, we are aware of that, and this is our second recommendation," the consultant said. "If you want to be relevant to the industry in the next decade, you must change your business model from hourly rates to value-based pricing. Our research shows that your clients want the design to be done faster at a lower price, and this is exactly why more and more general contractors win design projects. They have invested in design technologies more than you have."

Magda looked at James and said, "James, we've got to do something about this."

"Magda, we are an employee-owned company, and our principals are against these types of changes in our business model," James replied. "Bringing in new technology could potentially mean laying off people who own the company. This is insane. I think we should take the sustain strategy. We've been running the business like this for many years. Let's keep innovating like we have been, and find improvement opportunities in the company like we used to. Why drastically change things that are not broken yet?"

Magda said, "Or maybe we should have an offense strategy to open a new design division for data centers. People told me that we always talked about it, but we never entered that market. It could be a good time to kick off this division and reinvent how data centers should be designed."

It is clear from this story that James, Magda, and the consultant have different business strategies in mind. The consultant recommends a defense strategy, James is thinking about the sustain strategy, and Magda is thinking about taking the offense strategy by entering a new market.

What would you recommend to James and Magda? To go to a new market and take the offense approach, sustain what they have been doing, or defend against the insurgents?

Regardless of whether you take the offense, defense, or sustain strategy, you should innovate to be relevant to the market. This is where innovation with AI comes in. As discussed in earlier chapters, AI is a powerful tool that could be used to innovate and do things differently. But ultimately, your AI projects should serve your business strategy no matter what it is.

That's why, in this chapter, you will first identify your business strategy, and then learn about the AI augmentation framework and how to find AI use cases in line with that strategy.

Identify your business strategy

A business strategy is what allows people in an organization to prioritize tasks, make decisions, and take actions to achieve desired business goals. In an article for *Harvard Business Review* called "Demystifying Strategy: The What, Who, How, and Why," Michael D. Watkins, author of *The First 90 Days* and *Master Your Next Move*, says:

> *"A business strategy is a set of guiding principles that, when communicated and adopted in the organization, generates a desired pattern of decision-making. A strategy is about how people throughout the organization should make decisions and allocate resources to accomplish key objectives. A good strategy provides a clear roadmap, consisting of a set of guiding principles or rules, that defines the actions people in the business should take (and not take) and the things they should prioritize (and not prioritize) to achieve desired goals."* [19]

But why do you need a strategy?

Perhaps your company has an established line of business working in different project types (e.g., commercial, residential, industrial, infrastructure) or competing in various regions (e.g., your state, country, or internationally) to get projects in different sizes. This market is changing over time, and you need to align your resources to respond in the best way to those market moves. Otherwise, you will be irrelevant in the next decade or so.

Winning projects in these different market segments is its own game. Therefore, you may need to have a different strategy for different markets. In each of your market segments, you can choose to adopt an offense, defense, or sustain position. You are probably familiar with these concepts, but let's briefly discuss them before we go on.

A sustain strategy (also known as "business-as-usual") is used when

160

you are happy with where you are and what you do in the market, and want to safely stay put. You can use this strategy after a quick period of growth or after your defense or offense strategy has been completed. You can also use this strategy for continuous innovation and improvements over time, just to keep up with other competitors in the market. For the rest of this book, I will assume that the sustain strategy is the latter case: continuous innovation and improvements over time.

A defense strategy is used when you are under attack by a competitor. Say a new player in the market can do what you do cheaper and faster, and is winning projects that you ought to win. You need to defend your position, and your strategy is to defuse the threat and focus on what you do best. You must laser-focus on improving efficiencies and increasing productivity, or else you lose the battle.

An offense strategy is appropriate when *you* are the insurgent, and want to add a new line of business, go into a new market, or add a major capability that puts others in the market in danger. In this case, you are creating a unique business opportunity for your company that could potentially be part of your core offerings in the future.

Knowing your strategy in the market is essential in identifying how innovation, technology and, more specifically, AI can help you achieve your business goals. The alignment between your business strategy and your AI projects can be facilitated using the AI augmentation framework, which we will discuss next.

AI augmentation framework

The AI augmentation framework aligns your short- and long-term business strategy with your AI projects across your company. Based on your current business strategy, you can use this framework to discover, prioritize, build, and scale the opportunities that serve your business.

Inspired by Geoffrey A. Moore's book *Zone to Win: Organizing to*

Compete in an Age of Disruption, I created the AI innovation framework presented in Figure 7-1.

The framework has four quadrants, representing the four phases of your AI implementation journey. It starts from the "Ponder" phase at the top left, then goes through "Invent," "Innovate," and "Augment."

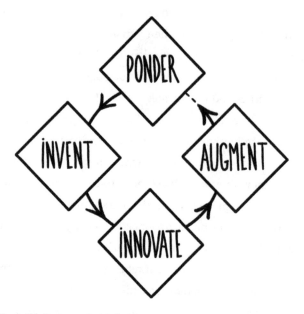

Figure 7-1: AI augmentation framework

Activities in the Ponder phase are related to finding the right AI use case (you will learn more about these activities in this chapter). The outcome of this phase is one or a few opportunities that you can use in the Invent phase. Activities in the Invent phase are related to creating proofs-of-concept and prototypes to validate the technical feasibility of your ideas. Then, in the Innovate phase, you pilot your prototype and test it in various projects. As a result, you may scale your technology solution across the company. This is how, in the Augment phase, you can enhance your staff and business capabilities.

Company executives often ask me about the time that it takes to get the return on investment of their AI project. Let me explain using the duration or time horizon by which your return on investment might be realized (Figure 7-2). Please use these horizons as a guide only, as their exact duration in real life will depend on the problem you want to solve.

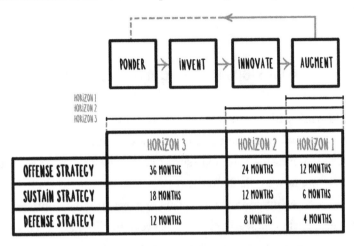

Figure 7-2: Time horizons for offense, sustain, and defense strategies

Let's start with the offense strategy. You want to enter a new market in the next three years, and you find AI use cases that help achieve your ambitious business goals. Once these opportunities are defined and prioritized, you can determine AI projects that support your business goals and expected outcomes. In this case, your Horizon 3 will be three years, followed by two years for Horizon 2 and one year for Horizon 1. In other words, it will be three years from the day that you started your Invent phase until you can scale the initiative in your business and get the return on investment.

When you are defending, all your focus should be on aligning your entire organization to solve existing business problems, and you'll be on an expedited version of Invention and Innovation activities. Depending on the attack, you may want to unify all your resources to stabilize your market position in less than a year.

In the sustain strategy, since you are not under attack, your time horizons will be somewhere between the time horizons for the offense and defense strategies.

Now that you know the time it takes to get your return on investment, let's get into the details of how you can prioritize the right AI use case to start your AI journey.

Four steps to the right AI use case

When I work with executives and CEOs, I often hear them say, "We know exactly what we want to do." Then, after finishing the workshop and brainstorming ideas, they are surprised by how many more relevant use cases are now available to them.

Often, company innovation leaders or executives have only one or two ideas for their first AI project. The problem with having a limited number of ideas is that you may face some technical or non-technical challenges down the road when you start implementing the project. Examples of technical problems are data that is segregated, unlabeled, or not even available, while examples of non-technical issues are limited time, budget, or lack of the right resources and skills. As a result, the project becomes too expensive to complete and provides little or no return on investment. So, you need to start with a list of AI use cases in order to find the right one. To do that, you need to take the four steps illustrated in Figure 7-3, all of which are part of the Ponder phase of the AI augmentation framework.

Let's look at each step now. Before that, though, I want to remind you that, as I mentioned in the introduction, this book has an accompanying workbook in which I have included some activities that you can perform with your team in half-day or full-day workshops. You can read through this chapter and the rest of the book, then return to these activities when you are implementing the steps laid out here. You can download the workbook for free at www.augmentit-book.com.

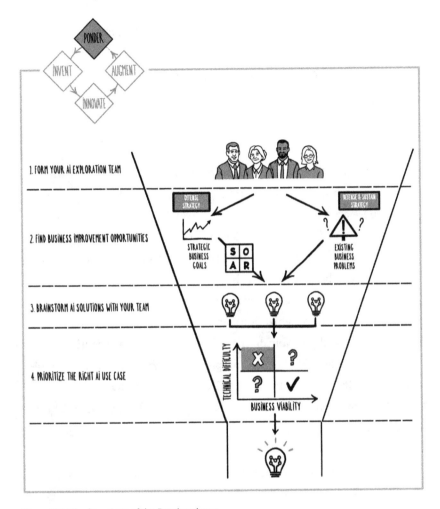

Figure 7-3: The four steps of the Ponder phase

1. Form your AI exploration team

The task of your AI brainstorming team is to find many different ideas for opportunities to use AI in your organization.

But why do you need a team to do it?

In Chapter 5, you learned that all AI systems have biases because humans build them, and all humans have unconscious biases.

---

*If you want to lessen your personal biases, cover
your blind spots, and find a diverse set of
ideas, you need to brainstorm with a team.*

Who's on the team?

Who you should brainstorm with depends on your goal and where
you want to find AI use cases. If you want to find AI use cases in sales
(and there are tons of use cases, by the way!), you will mainly need to
bring in people from the sales department.

Generally speaking, you should think of recruiting people from one
or two levels above you (whose buy-in or general support is needed, or
who can authorize your budget), your peers (if you want to find AI use
cases across your organization), and people one or two levels below
you (who should probably do the work or support the execution of it).

At the highest level of the company, the team could be the combination of CEO, CFO, CTO, CMO, CIO, and other CXOs.

In terms of background and skills, you need people from three
domains:

- **Business**: people who know your business problems, company
  vision, and future direction.
- **Technology**: people who understand the technology and know
  how it could be applied to business problems. They may or may
  not know about the ins and outs of AI.
- **Translator**: an internal AI lead or an external consultant who
  understands business problems and can find potential AI solutions for them.

One key factor in having a good exploration team is diversity. You
need a group that is diversified in age, gender, ethnicity, race, and mindset.

Think about bringing people from different personality types: detail-oriented and big-picture thinkers, introverts and extroverts.

By bringing this diverse team together, you'll be equipped with resources and ideas to propel you in your company's AI journey. It might be a lot of work to bring all these people together to explore ideas, but I promise you, it'll pay off in the long run.

Activity 1: Complete "Form your AI exploration team" in the workbook.

Now that you have formed your team, it's time to find those AI use cases.

2. Find business improvement opportunities

Depending on your business strategy, you may choose to find business improvement opportunities from your existing business problems (defense or sustain strategies) or from your strategic business goals (offense strategy). Let me explain.

Defense and sustain strategies

When you are defending, your goal becomes optimizing your current operating model to increase productivity and improve efficiencies in your current business. In this case, your AI use cases will be related to supporting your products or services, or could also be found in the back end of your business (e.g., sales, marketing, human resources, finance, legal). For instance, you might want to augment your sales force by narrowing down potential projects and finding the ones that you have a higher chance of winning. The goal of using AI in your existing projects could be improving the efficiency and effectiveness of your operation, or enhancing quality and safety to improve your bottom line.

Similar to defense strategy, when you are looking to sustain the status quo, your AI use cases can be found in your existing business problems.

Offense strategy

When you are entering into a new market, you will most likely want to add new capabilities to expand your current offerings. So instead of finding AI use cases among your existing problems, you should find them on the path that your company is taking into the future. In this chapter, you'll learn how to find those use cases by using a strategic planning and thinking framework called SOAR to identify your business' Strengths, Opportunities, Aspirations, and Results (see Figure 7-4).

In their book *Learning to SOAR: Creating Strategy that Inspires Innovation and Engagement*, Jacqueline M. Stavros and Gina Hinrichs describe four strategic conversations that you should have with your team:

> *"Focusing on strengths means that strategic conversations start with addressing what an individual, team, department, or organization is doing well. Strengths conversations explore what capabilities could be enhanced and what is compelling to those who have a stake in the organization's success. The second conversation is about opportunities to determine what possibilities are: new ideas, markets, products, services, and other innovations. The third conversation creates shared images – a vision of a future based on aspirations. This conversation centers on what might be and identifies which aspirations have the greatest potential to enable the vision to become a reality. The final conversation is about results; how will we know when we are succeeding and making a positive difference? What are the meaningful outcomes?"* [20]

Why use SOAR and not other well-established frameworks such as SWOT (Strengths, Weaknesses, Opportunities, Threats)? Because, unlike traditional strategic planning frameworks that are employed only by senior executives and then communicated to middle management and employees, SOAR invites various stakeholders to participate in the planning in order to define shared aspirations and values. By sharing their thoughts, challenges, and concerns, these stakeholders will become part of the plan and contribute to the execution and success of the goals set. Unlike SWOT, SOAR is a forward-thinking framework that focuses on the positive elements of SWOT (i.e., strengths and opportunities), extends them by exploring new possibilities arising from organizational aspirations, and considers where your company should go instead of just analyzing current threats and negative forces in the market.

Figure 7-4: The SOAR framework

Let's talk about each quadrant of the SOAR framework.

- **Strength (your greatness):** this is what separates your organization from your competitors. The most powerful strength of your organization, such as a strong balance sheet, brand, or work quality, comes from the things that you do well.
- **Opportunities (new possibilities):** business opportunities are chances for you to do something great in your organization. The source of the opportunity could be a change in the market, availability of new technology, or other trends either outside

or inside your business. Leveraging these opportunities at the right time can potentially give you a competitive advantage and a leading position in the market.

- **Aspirations (your dreams):** these are your biggest wishes and most ambitious dreams for your organization. It is your vision, an expression of what you want your business to be in the future. You need to consider your strengths and opportunities to come up with your goals.
- **Results (outcomes):** these are the tangible and measurable outcomes of your attempt to realize your goals, such as increasing your market share or improving your profitability.

To put this into context, I have prepared below a list of questions (Table 7-1) and examples of answers to those questions (Table 7-2).

Activity 2: Complete "Find opportunities for improving your business" in the workbook.

STRENGTH	OPPORTUNITIES
• What do we excel at? • What makes us unique? • What is our proudest achievement?	• What are the best opportunities for our company? • What are the new markets, and what new products and services can we offer? • What are the unfulfilled needs of our customers?
ASPIRATIONS	RESULTS
Considering our strength and business opportunities: • What do we care and are passionate about? • How can we make a big difference? • What does our company look like five years from now?	Considering the goals that we have: • What are our metrics for measuring and tracking our progress towards our goals? • How do we translate our bold vision into measurable outcomes? • How do we know if a goal is achieved?

Table 7-1: List of SOAR questions [21]

STRENGTH	OPPORTUNITIES
• Leading in hospital design and construction in North America. • Increasing our sales and revenue year after year. • Having one of the best staff training programs in the industry.	• Increasing our market share in developing countries. • Improving our profitability. • Improving our workforce development program.
ASPIRATIONS	**RESULTS**
• Becoming number one in hospital design and construction worldwide. • Becoming super-efficient in delivering our projects and services. • Serving our staff and clients to win "Best Company of the Year" in the AEC awards!	• Increasing revenue by 20% globally year-over-year. • Reducing our operational costs by 10% year-over-year. • Improve our staff engagement score by 5% every quarter.

Table 7-2: An example of SOAR for a design and construction company

3. Brainstorm AI solutions with your team

The improvement opportunities that you found in your existing projects or strategic business goals by using the SOAR framework give you a starting point for your brainstorming session with your AI exploration team.

You probably know a lot more about your projects, your company, and the problems you have than you know about AI solutions. That's okay: at this step, you should not be looking for a perfect AI solution. Instead, you should facilitate a brainstorming session and discussion to find out how you may use AI in achieving some of your business goals or improvement opportunities. To do so, you can convert your business goals and opportunities into "how might we" questions. For instance, if the business problem or goal you want to address is, "increase our revenue by 10% year-over-year," by adding "how might we" at the beginning and turning it into a question, you'll have: "How might we use AI to increase our revenue by 10% year-over-year?"

"How might we" statements are really powerful for several reasons.

The "how" part suggests that you don't have an answer yet, and you need to explore the problem and ideate on finding novel solutions. The "might" part suggests that there could be multiple different ways to solve the problem. By ideating, brainstorming, and exploring various points of view from the individuals in the team, you are set to innovate and find new solutions. The "we" part suggests that you are part of a team, and you should work together to understand the problem and come up with multiple potential solutions.

After converting your improvement goals or opportunities into "how might we" statements, it's time to start your brainstorming session. Like the previous activity, spend ten to twenty minutes for individual ideations before running your share-out session, in which individuals explain their three to five most important ideas to the rest of the team.

As a result of this brainstorming session, you create lots of ideas, some of which are repetitive and have overlaps. To narrow down the ideas you find, you can group them into buckets or clusters based on their similarities. For instance, all the revenue-related ideas can go into one cluster called "Revenue." Once clustered, you can ask the team to vote for the top six clusters or individual ideas.

Why only six ideas? As you will see in the next step, you need to do due diligence on these ideas to find the right AI use cases for implementation. If you bring lots of ideas to the next step, you'll need a long time for the due diligence. If you bring just one or two ideas, you may eliminate your chance of finding the right use case. Six is a number that I have found hits just the right balance between too many and too few, but feel free to use whatever number you think works best for you.

Activity 3: Complete "Brainstorm AI solutions with your team" in the workbook.

4. Prioritize the right AI use case

As a result of the brainstorming session with your team, clustering your ideas, and voting, you should now have your top six ideas. The question is, which one is the best idea for implementation?

You may ask, "Why not just pick the idea with the highest vote?" The reason the idea with the highest vote may not be the right use case is that it might be too difficult to implement. In other words, we need to find an idea that is very important but also easy to implement.

The importance/difficulty matrix is one of the design thinking methods that we use in this step (see Figure 7-5). The four quadrants of the matrix help you to find the right AI implementation opportunity. The right AI use case is in the bottom right quadrant, and is called "quick wins." These are the use cases that rank high in importance, but low in difficulty. Use cases on the top right quadrant are "major strategic projects." These are very important for your company, but also difficult to implement. The top left quadrants represent "luxury" projects, which are of low importance and high difficulty. You should avoid these projects as much as you can. The projects on the lower left quadrant are "low-priority" projects. Even though these projects are less difficult to do, their relatively low importance puts them on the less-preferred project list.

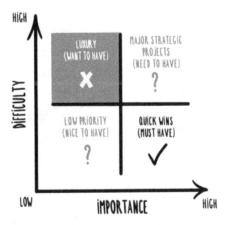

Figure 7-5: Importance/difficulty matrix

If you start with very difficult projects, even if they are very strategic and important, you may not achieve the expected results, and you can underwhelm your sponsors and stakeholders. If you are just starting your AI journey, try to focus on "quick wins" to improve morale and build momentum for successful future projects.

Now that you know what an importance/difficulty matrix is and how you will use it, it's time to talk about how to assess the importance and difficulty of each idea.

The importance of an idea could be assessed by how viable it is for your business to invest in it; in other words, we look at the return on investment for each idea. The difficulty of an idea could be assessed by its technical feasibility.

The right AI use case is a use case that is both a viable investment and a technically feasible idea.

I'd like to note that business viability and technical feasibility are just two ways to evaluate the importance and difficulty of your ideas. You may consider other evaluation criteria or metrics as well: for instance, instead of calculating your return on investment, you may have metrics that measure sustainability, social, or environmental impacts. You can choose how you'd like to measure the importance or difficulty with one or a combination of your metrics.

Nick Bagatelos, former president of Bagatelos Architectural Glass Systems, shared with me some other ways you can evaluate your AI use cases:

"The return from your investment cannot be measured only with dollars and monetary values. The payback could be the learning

that comes from your projects or the adoption rate from the people who want to use the technology."

Technical feasibility

A feasible use case is a use case that is technically possible. One unfeasible idea that I often hear in workshops is, "We want AI to read the market, predict the future, and tell us where to invest in the next three years." Counterfactual!!! This is not possible – even we, as humans, cannot tell with certainty what the future will be.

You need to assess the feasibility of AI use cases because ideas that are very difficult to implement are not good candidates for your first AI project. These challenging ideas may need a long period of research and development, and frequently they don't yield reasonable solutions. So you may spend a lot of time, money, and energy getting a mediocre solution.

The good news is that you don't need to have a precise answer on how technically feasible your idea is. You are at the early stage of the project, and just knowing the relative difficulty of the AI use case can help you make a better decision on which AI use case is the right one to start with. Let's go back to the AI tree in Chapter 3 for a moment: if, for instance, your AI use case lies within the machine learning branch of AI, having a structured and high-quality dataset might make the opportunity easier to implement than if you had an unstructured and low-quality dataset.

Because of all these nuances, I try not to give any general advice about the relative difficulties of various branches of AI. Therefore, to assess the technical feasibility of your ideas you should work with people who have done AI projects. These internal or external consultants can advise you on how difficult it is to develop a solution for the idea.

You can be creative about how you score the relative difficulty of each idea. You can use a three-scale rating (low, medium, and high difficulty), a star-rating system (one star being low difficulty, five stars being extremely difficult), or you can even measure the difficulty by assessing how long it takes to build a solution (e.g., six months for idea #1, twelve months for idea #2).

Activity 4: Complete "Assess technical feasibility" in the workbook.

At this point, you should know roughly how feasible each of your AI use cases is. Now, we will take a deeper look into how viable each AI use case might be for your business.

Feasibility: is it technically possible to implement this use case?

Business viability

A viable use case is a use case that creates a high return on investment (ROI) given your business and financial constraints.

Some AI use cases are highly desirable, but have less ROI because they need significant capital investment. You should stay away from low-ROI ideas if you want to leverage AI to gain a competitive advantage. Imagine a scenario in which you spend a million dollars developing an AI solution that could give you a million-dollar return over the next ten years. I'd invest that money somewhere else.

A good AI problem brings at least five times more value to the company than the original investment.

Activity 5: Complete "Assess ROI and business viability" in the workbook.

At this point, you should know how feasible and viable each AI use case is for your company. Now it's time to put everything together to find the right AI use case. Again, the ideal use case is at the intersection of technical feasibility (which you identified based on how difficult it is to implement the solution) and viability (which you determined based on your ROI calculation). In other words, you are looking for a use case that is important to your company, easy to achieve, and generates value for your business.

Viability: should you invest in this use case?

To find that use case, you need to arrange each opportunity based on its relative importance on the X-axis of the importance/difficulty matrix (Figure 7-5). Once all the use cases are placed, you should then move them along the Y-axis based on their relative difficulty. Remember, the ideas on the bottom right quadrant ("quick wins"), should be considered for your first AI project.

Activity 6: Complete "Identify the right AI use case" in the workbook.

Congratulations! You found the right use case to start your AI journey. Before moving to the next chapter to develop a solution for it, you should do one optional but highly recommended activity.

Often, the AI exploration team is not the same as the execution team. Typically, senior management forms the exploration team, while researchers, scientists, or even external consultants are part of the execution team. Therefore, it is crucial to document what you have discussed and communicate the project expectations with your sponsors and the execution team. That's why, in the workbook, I created an AI project planning document that I highly recommend you complete with your team.

Activity 7: Complete "Plan your AI project" in the workbook.

KEY TAKEAWAYS

- Good AI use cases are closely tied to business problems.
- The AI augmentation framework has four major phases in three time horizons.
- The Ponder phase has activities for finding and prioritizing the right AI use case.
- To reduce biases, you need a diverse team of managers, peers, and executors in your exploration team.
- Using the SOAR framework, you can find business improvement goals or opportunities by looking into your business' strengths, opportunities, aspirations, and results.
- You need to do technical and business due diligence before the solution development phase.
- The right AI use case is the one that is easiest to achieve and will give the highest return on investment.

EMBRACE CHANGE TO BREAK THE STATUS QUO

Hilda Espinal is the chief technology officer at CannonDesign, one of the ten most innovative design firms in the world according to *Fast Company*. With more than twenty-five years of experience in architectural and technology development for AEC, she leads a team of developers and digital experts to create innovative solutions for design challenges. I had a discussion with her about how we should find opportunities for using AI in business problems. Here is what she shared with me:

We often hear people in our industry say, 'Don't change what isn't broken.' I, instead, encourage them to embrace change as being richer in opportunities than the inconveniences of breaking the status quo. AI is here to make our business more profitable, help us design better, and consequently have a more significant and positive impact on the built environment, ultimately making the way we live, play, and work better.

To bring AI to your company, you need to bring together the company's business leaders (e.g., CEO, CFO, CMO) and technology leaders (e.g., CTO, CIO). One of the challenges in the AEC industry is that these two groups do not necessarily speak the same language. In other words, people who run AEC companies and define where the business is going often have misconceptions about technological capabilities and AI. Therefore, AI education becomes the centerpiece and first step in any AI project.

Our industry leaders must demystify AI and understand what it really is. The next step after education is exploring what AI means to you, your group, or your company. How is AI going to help you achieve your business goals? Discussing these questions can help us understand why you want to do an AI project.

Once you know about the 'why' and business goals, you need people who can translate it into achievable AI projects and get everybody on the same page. The primary role of this translator is to convert business goals into how we might use AI in achieving them (potential AI solutions). That person must be knowledgeable about AI and know how to communicate it with the firm's leadership and get their buy-in. That 'business problem-to-AI solution' translator could be an individual inside the company, or a consultant who speaks both the business and technical language.

I highly recommend you start from the quick-win projects. These success stories will interest stakeholders and build confidence to ultimately empower you to try more challenging projects. So, in your next project, you win more people over and expand on it.

Or, if your first project was not as successful as you expected, do a postmortem on it and see how it is received – sharing what did not work and why can guide the stakeholders who may have unrealistic expectations about what AI can do. It creates more conversation, interest, curiosity, and further education in the company. Then you can decide if you want to continue that path or start another quick-win project.

CHAPTER 8

Build the solution right

A few years ago I met an executive of a construction company who told me, "We've done lots of experimentations with AI, and we did not get any good outcomes from them." I was curious, and asked a lot of questions about the problems they wanted to solve and how they built solutions. Here is the summary of my investigation on how they created a solution:

"We put one of the best construction managers on our AI project. He secured the budget and hired three interns to kick off our AI project. After three weeks of work, he didn't see any good results, so he decided to switch to another project. Again, after a month of work, the interns could not show us anything promising, and then they had to go back to school."

When I heard this story, I remembered a quote by Chris Sacca from the show *Shark Tank*:

"Ideas are cheap; execution is everything."

Executives of companies that are unsuccessful in running AI projects often hire a data scientist or intern to report to them directly, thinking that this is the best way they can learn about AI. Unfortunately, they don't have the time and knowledge to guide their AI intern or scientist. And this is a recipe for disaster.

Executives of companies that are successful in running AI projects provide the right support and an environment for other staff to create AI teams or organizations. They work with the head of their AI team, but never try to manage their AI scientists directly.

That's why, in this chapter, you'll learn about how to run your first AI project like a champion, using the steps shown in Figure 8-1. In the previous chapter, you learned about the Ponder phase of the AI augmentation framework, which concluded with you prioritizing the right opportunity. In this chapter, you'll learn about taking this opportunity into the Invent, Innovate, and Augment phases of the framework so that you can build your solution right.

Invent

In the previous chapter, you prioritized AI use cases based on their business viability and technical feasibility. Compared to other industries, AI is untested and relatively new to our industry. Therefore, you should expect that some of the solution ideas may not work as expected, and this means that you need to test them as fast as possible. The phrase "fail often, fail fast" really applies to this phase. The main goal of this phase is to validate the technical feasibility of your AI solutions, and it typically takes a few weeks to several months, depending on the complexity of the project. This phase has three major activities: forming your AI execution team; crossing the knowledge chasm between you and your execution team; and validating the technical feasibility of your idea by prototyping.

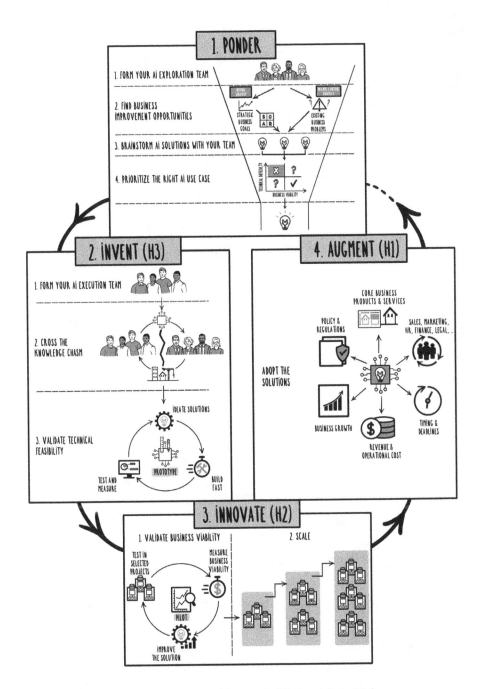

Figure 8-1: Ponder, Invent, Innovate, Augment (phases to build your solutions right)

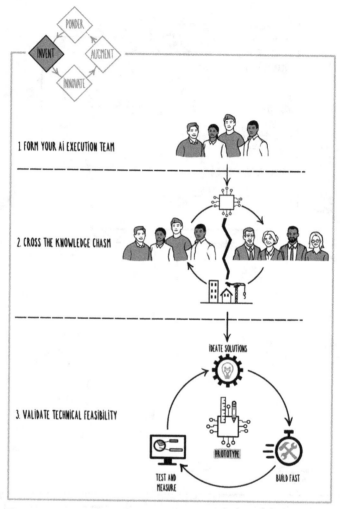

Figure 8-2: Invent phase

1. Form your AI execution team

The AI execution team is the team that helps you develop your AI solution. Some members of your AI exploration team – those you worked with to find the right use case, as described in the previous chapter – could potentially be in the AI execution team; for instance, you may have a chief scientist or AI engineer who helped you assess the technical feasibility of each idea, who can also help with the execution

BUILD THE SOLUTION RIGHT

of the project. In general, however, people in the AI exploration team are business leaders and decision-makers with less technical skills than the members of the execution team, who might have researchers and scientists who do the implementation work. This execution team could be internal to your company, or external.

Let's discuss both of these options in detail.

Having your own team

You can hire your own AI team, whose members become employees of your company. Your AI team could be one or multiple people with a background in data science, machine learning, optimization, and various other branches of AI.

What are some of the opportunities and challenges of having your own AI team?

Opportunity: Control and access. The benefit of having your own AI team is that you have more control and freedom over what you do. You have access to them at any time during execution of the project, and their learnings stay in your organization. They also have the best access to subject-matter experts and the people they need to work with, and will understand your business problem and organization. They can work on super-confidential projects with data that you may not share with external partners.

Challenge 1: High salary and compensation. The downside of having an in-house AI team is the cost. In Silicon Valley, some tech companies are known to pay more than $500,000 in salary and compensations in order to hire senior machine learning engineers! For comparison, the average salary of a senior architect in the Bay Area is around $100,000, according to Glassdoor. While the salary and compensation of AI researchers and scientists in your area may not be as crazy high as the machine learning engineers of Silicon Valley, in general, these experts are in very high demand. You can go to a site like Glassdoor to find out how much the average salary of an AI engineer or data scientist in your area is.

Challenge 2: Talent acquisition and retention. It is very difficult for AEC companies to compete with the tech companies' salary and demand generation engine. This means that you may end up hiring not-so-great talents, or good ones who may leave after a short period to work for the tech companies. Eric Law, senior director of innovation at Swinerton, offered his view on this issue:

> "Hiring and maintaining top AI talents are major challenges for our industry. The higher-end AI experts or sharp students who graduated from the top universities don't want to work for the AEC companies. Their first choice is going to tech companies like Google or Amazon, or even working in the manufacturing industry."

Challenge 3: Diverse experience. Besides the cost and difficulty of finding talent, another downside of having an in-house AI team is a lack of diverse experience. I cannot tell you how many companies I have worked with because their data scientists could not find a reasonable solution for their machine learning or optimization problem. I found that many AEC companies hire just one or two junior data scientists to run their AI projects. The problem, as you learned in Part 2, is that there are various AI techniques, and complex AEC problems often require using a combination of these. So, your first couple of hires must have a diverse background in AI (AI generalist) rather than knowing a particular branch of AI in depth (AI specialist). Besides your core AI team, you may also need a diverse technical team that includes experts such as data engineers or architects, UX designers, and developers in order to bring your AI solution to life. Jit Kee Chin, chief data and innovation officer at Suffolk, says:

"Developing an AI solution in your company is like building a building. Similar to buildings, an 'AI solution' isn't necessarily built by one person – therefore, hiring one data scientist is not the answer. Similar to buildings, AI has various branches and sub-specialties. To develop the right solution, you need a team to support your AI scientists or engineers, so that the solution can both be developed and drive the impact you're looking for. In addition to data scientists, you need data engineers to wrangle data, visualization experts to communicate the findings intuitively, developers to productize the solution, potentially a data architect to put in place the right infrastructure, and, critically, the business and subject-matter experts who can clearly define the use case and embed the solution once it's developed. It is not as simple as saying, 'Let's hire a data scientist,' though some of these talents may exist elsewhere in the business. Don't underestimate the job and what it takes to do it."

Complex and multidisciplinary AEC projects demand a multidisciplinary team. Therefore, you should build a team with a diverse background in various branches of AI, such as optimization, machine learning, and reasoning, in addition to software engineers and visualization experts.

Hiring an AI consultant

Hiring an AI consulting company that can partner with you and help you better understand various AI use cases or run a few AI experiments might be the cheaper and more reliable way to get your feet wet.

What are some opportunities and challenges of hiring an AI consultant?

Opportunity: Diverse experience. Consultants often have a diverse AI team, and are not biased towards using just one specific branch of AI to solve problems. The cost of hiring a consultant to run a project might be a lot less compared to the cost of hiring your own AI talent and building an in-house team. Because of their experience and knowledge of the domain, consultants are more likely to deliver higher-quality solutions than an in-house AI team.

Challenge: Disconnection. The downside of working with a consultant is that you might be hands-off while the consultant is doing the project for you. Therefore, you won't gain the knowledge of how to execute an AI project.

One way of dealing with this problem is having frequent update reviews with your consultant and using the learning from this book to ask questions about the implementation of the project.

The verdict?

Here is my recommendation to CEOs and business executives: if you have done a couple of AI experiments, have a long-term AI vision, enough budget, and are looking for long-term gains, you should have your own AI team. If you are looking for short-term gains, want to find the right AI use cases, or just want to run your first AI experiment, hire an AI consultant.

Do you want to work with consultants to start your AI projects and then hire a team, or do you wish to have your own team from the beginning?

Now that you have an execution team, let's move on to the second step.

2. Cross the knowledge chasm

People often ask me what is the most challenging part of running an AI project. The answer is this step – crossing an enormous chasm of knowledge.

On one side of the chasm, you are an AEC expert who knows the industry and the problem your company is facing. However, you may not know much about AI and the science behind it. On the other side of the chasm are your AI execution team members, who, most of the time, are from the data or computer science domain and do not have any background in AEC. Even though they know a lot about AI, they may not be familiar with the AEC industry, and they do not understand your problem from the outset. It is as if one side speaks one language and the other speaks another. That's why crossing this chasm is a crucial step that makes or breaks a project.

How do you cross that chasm? The only way is by each side educating the other about their respective domains. You need to educate your AI team about the AEC business problem you are trying to solve, why this is a problem, and the business impact you and the company's executives expect from this project. You need to elaborate on the AI use case, and initiate some discussions with your AI exploration team in this step.

Remember, you are doing your first AI project to learn about and get to know AI, so treat your AI execution team as a partner, not an employee. Revisit Part 2 of this book to find questions to ask them about their approach to learning more – that way you are getting to know their world and language, and teaching them your AEC expertise and knowledge. By the time you get to the second or third project, your team knows more about AEC and you have learned a lot more about AI and what it can or cannot do.

But before that, you have some challenges ahead. Beware!

Let's review what you and your team need to do and the outcome expected from this phase.

What do you do?

Prepare a debrief. At this phase of the project, you should summarize all the discussions and documents you created about the projects in the previous chapter. You should prepare yourself to discuss with your team all the activities that you have done in the earlier steps, from ideation to prioritization. For instance, why was this project feasible, desirable, and viable for the company to invest in? What were the other projects and finalists, and why was this one chosen from among them?

You should share the planning document that I described at the end of the previous chapter if you have completed it. As I said, this document is optional but highly recommended.

Gather requirements. You should also prepare what the requirements of the project are. What is it that you want to build, what are the specifications? What do the success criteria look like at the end of the project from your company's point of view? How do you test the solution against the success criteria?

Answers to some of these questions might not be evident, but it's good to prepare yourself if they come up in the onboarding meeting, which is one of the significant activities in this phase.

Onboard the team. The onboarding meeting is a half-day workshop that you should schedule with your AI team. In this meeting, you invite guest speakers from project sponsors and people who are experiencing the problem you are trying to solve. A talk from the CEO or other highly regarded executives could be an excellent way to kick off the workshop, followed by a talk about the problem by people who deal with it every day so that they can show their workflow. For instance, if you want to improve the design process, bring in the designer to talk about how tedious drawing production is and demonstrate how it is done today. This way, your team can learn about the process and observe where the challenges are with their own eyes. These things might be obvious to you, but not to your AI execution team.

Once your team has an overall understanding of the project, it's time to give them weekly doses of the process associated with the problem that you want them to solve.

You should do this because your team needs to fully understand how you are dealing with the problem today and what the root causes of the problem are. Don't just tell them what the process is or what the inefficiencies are; they must see it for themselves.

Let me tell you a story to illustrate my point. I used to lead a research team to develop AI solutions for the structural engineering domain. I told them many times and in different ways what the problems were. One day, I scheduled a one-hour meeting with a structural engineer so that my team could watch how structural design and analysis are performed and direct their questions to the engineer. The one-hour meeting ended eight hours later, because the structural engineer walked them through various projects to show them his struggles in modeling and designing buildings. The result? They came out of the meeting saying, "Now we understand exactly what the problem is."

Show your team what the problem is; do not just tell them.

What does your team do?

Document and reflect. Your team is still learning about the problem and perhaps the industry at this point. One of the best ways to accelerate their learning is by asking them to document the problem and the current process, and then reflect on what they learned. You can ask them to do research on the problem and present their findings to you in their own words. Then you can review their presentations and reflection to see how much they learned and what the gaps are.

Ideate. Once they get to know the current process and the problem in depth, your team's job is to look into how they may solve the problem. Ideation at this stage happens at a very high level. Your team needs to brainstorm how different AI techniques could possibly help with solving the problem.

Due diligence. Depending on the method they choose, your team will need to do some research and due diligence. For instance, if they want to use learning-based methods, they should look into the 5 Vs of data discussed in Chapter 4, especially its quality and quantity (e.g., how many data samples are available? Are they labeled?). They can run a quick test on data to learn more about its distribution and how good or bad it is. For the optimization-based methods, they may need to look into the goals and constraints of the problem to see how they need to compute it. Some metrics like time and cost might be easier to calculate than subjective metrics like esthetics.

At the end of this stage, your team's deliverable is a document that contains the problem, potential solutions, and results of all the due diligence and interviews that they did with the subject-matter experts.

Now, it's time to develop your prototype.

3. Validate technical feasibility

In the Ponder phase, you assumed that this AI use case would be easy to achieve. At this step, you need to challenge that assumption. To validate the technical feasibility of your solution and minimize the risk of failure, you should create a prototype. Your AI prototype is a rudimentary working model of your final AI solution, with some limited functionalities. The goal is to quickly create a simpler version of your final solution and test it against the project requirements before investing too much time and too many resources.

The best way to build a prototype is by going through a few agile cycles of ideating conceptual solutions, technology-building, and measuring the outcome against the project goals (see Figure 8-2).

Let's talk about each of these in more detail.

Ideate solutions

It is very easy to default to one solution and start working on it. But beware: the first solution is often not the best solution. You will probably find a lot of better solutions (cheaper, faster, better quality) if you explore a number of ideas before defaulting to the first solution that comes to mind.

A common mistake people make in executing an AI project is to default to a specific solution without ideating and brainstorming various ways of solving the problem.

But how do you ideate conceptual solutions?

As you learned in the previous chapter, you can run a brainstorming session to facilitate a discussion among your team. One way of doing this ideation session is to ask your team to come up with one or a few solutions, and then write them out on a poster or large piece of paper. The poster can have the main solution idea, illustrating how it works, who it is for, what the risks are, and how to measure success. This visual is known as a concept poster.

Another way of ideating in this phase is by creating a table, with columns being steps or details of the problem and rows being the enabling technology (such as the various branches of the AI tree that we discussed in Chapter 3). For instance, if you want to develop an AI solution for the conceptual design phase of projects, your columns could be "volumetric design," "building core design," "façade design," and "layout design," and your rows would be "search and optimization," "machine learning," "knowledge representation and reasoning," or other branches of the AI tree. You can leave the last row as a wild card for any ideas outside the box to encourage creative solutions (see Figure 8-3). Each cell represents an idea from the intersection of the two categories. For instance, the ideas in the first intersection could be the answer to "How might we use search and optimization in the volumetric design of the building?" You should encourage your team members to generate ideas for each cell.

Once conceptual solutions are created, your team should present the concepts to your ideal target users and stakeholders to get their feedback. They should comment on what concepts they liked, what they didn't like, and where, from their point of view, the areas of opportunity are.

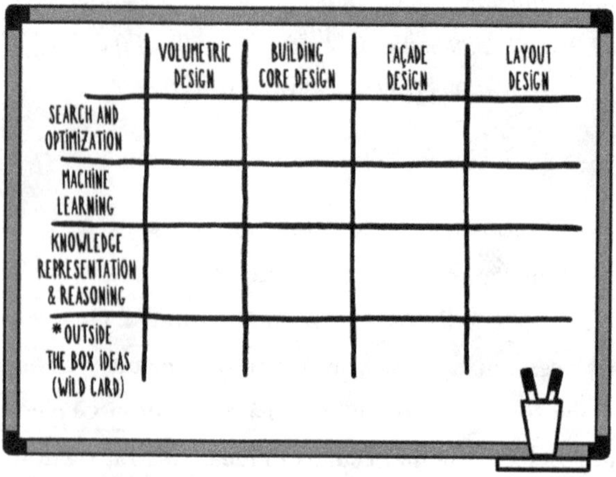

	VOLUMETRIC DESIGN	BUILDING CORE DESIGN	FAÇADE DESIGN	LAYOUT DESIGN
SEARCH AND OPTIMIZATION				
MACHINE LEARNING				
KNOWLEDGE REPRESENTATION & REASONING				
*OUTSIDE THE BOX IDEAS (WILD CARD)				

Figure 8-3: Creative matrix example

After getting feedback from your ideal users, your team should write a proposal on how to bring the concept poster to life!

The delivery, at the end of this phase, is the concepts, the feedback you received, and your team's proposal on how to bring these concepts to life. This proposal is essential in executing the next phase.

Now, it's time to build a solution.

Build fast

Your team generated lots of solution ideas, and they probably picked one or two that they are comfortable with or passionate about. Now what?

In this step, your team creates some proofs-of-concept to identify the feasibility of the AI method. Even though your team knows what the problem is, and they probably know how to solve the problem, they should test their solution as fast as possible, because the devil is always in the details! That's why I often call this step "agile experimentation." You don't know what is working, or how it is working, or what the quality of output is until you build it.

Based on the results of this agile experimentation and your proofs-of-concept, you can decide which AI solution or method has more potential to satisfy project requirements and stakeholders' expectations. Then, you need to help your team expand the solution and create a functional technology prototype. This prototype eventually becomes your AI solution in the future, after lots of testing and refinement.

At this point, you should have regular check-ins with your stakeholders, especially your end user, to share your progress and get their feedback. This is crucial to the success of your project.

Test and measure

All AI solutions have their own strengths and limitations. Testing gives you the power to know in which scenario the solution works, and what its limitations are. It gives you an idea of the boundaries of the solution and helps identify the lines that, if crossed, prevent your solution from yielding good results. Testing starts when you create your first prototype. Once created, you should test it for accuracy and against project requirements.

Testing is like a compass for your AI project: if you don't test rigorously, you may get lost and never recover. I was once asked to advise an AI team that could not get the results they wanted, and couldn't figure out why the AI solution returned really bad results. When I asked them to show me their validation process, I realized that they didn't have any test plan, or even a test case, to run the solution against. They could have avoided all the headaches and confusion if they had a testing plan from the beginning.

Ultimately, you want to test your solution on a real-world problem. But there is a huge difference between the capabilities of the first solution your team develops and the complexity of the real-world problem.

Testing is the responsibility of everyone. The AI team needs to test and validate their solution on their own. They are responsible for their own testing, which is mostly a target for the accuracy of the results. The AI project lead is responsible for testing the solution against the project requirements and business outcomes. For the rest of the chapter, I am assuming that you are the project lead. So, you and your team need to create two test problems: a case study and a toy problem. Let me explain each one in detail.

Create a case-study problem. Before testing your solution in a real-world project, you should prepare some tests in a controlled lab environment. You need a proxy or case-study problem because the real-world problems are either too complex as a starting point, or not well-documented enough for the researchers and engineers who want to develop a solution. A case-study problem is a slightly simplified and well-documented version of the real-world problem.

In the case study, you need to document the requirements and precisely what you want to achieve. In addition, you should write down the pass-or-fail criteria and how to measure the success of the research. You need to own the case-study document.

Create a toy problem. Once you have the case-study problem, you can pass it to the engineers and researchers to create a toy problem. A toy problem is a simplified version of the case-study problem used by your AI team in their everyday research and development. Having the case study and the requirements in mind, they should develop the algorithm that works on their simplified toy problem.

Let me share with you an example to put these testing methods in perspective. In one of my projects, my AI engineer developed a machine learning model for a ten-story commercial building. His toy problem was a one-story building measuring three meters by three meters with four columns and beams. We did a hand calculation of stress and displacements to verify the predictions from his machine learning model. So, every time he improved his machine learning model, he tested the new model against that simple problem to quickly measure how good or bad the new model was.

After a few rounds of testing on the toy problem to make sure his model worked on that, he sent me his latest machine learning model so that I could test it on my case-study problem. From his testing, his model had 80% accuracy. But what does that mean in the structural engineering practice? Is 80% accuracy good enough? When I tested it on my case-study problem, I found that, because of the 20% inaccuracy, I spent more time modifying the recommended AI design than I would have if I had just designed the structure from scratch without AI. Therefore, the time-saving and business outcome we wanted could not be achieved, which meant we had to go back to the drawing board. The point is that you must test your AI solution on the case-study problem to measure if the results are acceptable or not.

If the results need improvements (and most likely they will) or they are not acceptable, you need to go back to the ideate step and go through this cycle again. This time, you may pick a different idea and try to solve the problem from a different angle.

You are responsible for testing the solution against project requirements and business outcomes, while your team is responsible for testing the solution for accuracy and technical requirements.

To summarize: in the Invent phase, you ideated several conceptual solutions with your team, developed proofs-of-concept and a prototype that functioned as a proxy to your final AI solution, and measured how it performed using various test problems that you and your team created. By going through this cycle multiple times, you have validated the technical feasibility of your AI solution and are ready to test it in real-world problems.

In the next phase, you'll learn how to introduce your prototype to the world outside your lab!

Innovate

In the previous chapter, when you calculated the business viability of your AI solution, you made lots of assumptions about how it brings value to your company (e.g., reducing time, saving on cost, increasing quality, improving safety). Unlike the Invent phase, in which the goal was ideating solutions and performing agile experimentations to validate the technical feasibility, this phase focuses on validating the business viability of your AI solution. The reason you do this is because there is always a delta between the ideal AI solution that you had in mind in the Ponder phase, and the solution you actually built. For instance, your solution accuracy may not be good, or it may need lots of post-processing. Therefore, two major activities of the Innovate phase are validating the business viability, and scaling.

Validate business viability

The best way to validate the business viability of your AI solution is by going through the agile cycles of testing it in three to ten pilot projects. This allows you to improve it by gathering and implementing all the requirements and nuances of the projects, and measuring the solution's business viability (see Figure 8-4). This phase typically takes a few to several months to complete depending on your business strategy (offense, defense, or sustain).

Let's talk about each step in more detail.

Test in selected projects

It's time to take your AI solution out of the lab and test it in a few selected projects. This is because you want to capture all potential issues and address them before testing it in numerous different projects. If your solution does not work in one project, there is an excellent chance it won't work in other projects. If you roll out your solution to numerous projects in a broad range of settings too soon (while it is

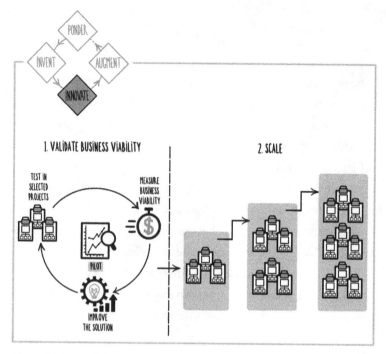

Figure 8-4: Innovate phase

not working properly in the test cases), you'll create chaos – both in those projects, and for your team.

How to test

At this step, you probably need to sit with your end user to test your solution. Depending on the solution's level of maturity, you may need to run it on behalf of the end user, or you can ask the end user to do it while you are there to educate them and answer questions. In both cases, the goal is to capture feedback about what is working and what is not working, and to find potential improvement areas.

Measure business viability

One of the differences between testing in the prototyping and piloting phase is measuring the solution against the business requirements of the project (i.e., business viability).

In this phase, you should measure how much the AI solution brings business value in reality. Let me give you an example. Let's say that your designer used to complete a design in five business days. Under the assumption that, with the help of AI, your designer can do it in one day, you measured the ROI and your project got approved. Then, you worked with your execution team and developed a solution. Next, you tested the AI solution in the pilot phase in three projects. Unfortunately, you realized that because of the slow speed in generation and the low quality of the solution, designers had to spend two days to generate outputs and three days improving the quality of the selected solution. So all in all, your designers won't save time, and they are very reluctant to use the AI solution. This solution does not deliver the business value that you projected.

In this case, you either need to stop the project, or improve the solution.

Improve the solution

Based on the results of the testing and the feedback received, you have a list of what worked well and what didn't work well, and a wish list. Based on the pattern that you find in testing the solution with different people in selected projects, you need to decide how to improve the solution.

You can use the importance/difficulty matrix again here (see Figure 7-5). You know what the importance of each request is based on your business goals, but you may not know how difficult they are to implement. That's why you should work with your execution team to give you feedback about the level of difficulty of each feature. Again, you are looking for quick wins – i.e., requests plotted on the bottom right of the importance/difficulty matrix.

Let me give you an example.

Let's say some of the feedback you received was related to increasing the accuracy of your machine learning model and reducing the time of generation of your optimization engine. While reducing the generation time could be done by parallelizing the computation (relatively easy), improving the accuracy of a machine learning model could be very difficult in the absence of high-quality data. If these two improvement requests are equally important, you may prioritize the "reducing the generation time" request over the "increasing the accuracy" request.

So, your ultimate job in this phase is to prioritize the requests you receive and make sure that your execution team develops them within the scope and timeframe you have.

If your solution meets business viability and technical feasibility requirements, it might be time to hit the road to scale!

Scale

Scaling your AI solution means making sure your solution is deployed and available to be used across your organization without your presence and hand-holding. This is how you can take the capabilities of your workforce to the next level.

Typically, depending on the scope and requirements, it takes at least one to two years (or even more) from the start of a project to get to the point that it is scaled across your organization. The scaling process is quite similar to piloting, but at a bigger scale.

In the scaling phase, you need to deploy your AI solution in an accessible environment, typically on a company's internal cloud or an external cloud provider. You should also integrate your solution with the rest of your company's IT infrastructure.

You should know that not all the AI solutions that graduate from pilot programs are worth scaling. One key factor in determining whether a solution is ready to scale or not is the satisfaction level of end users.

In both the prototyping and piloting steps, you should work closely with your end users to improve the solution based on their feedback. Once you get to a point where your users are very happy (and sometimes in love) with your solution – i.e., they trust the results, and you see a pull from them to use it in their projects – it's time to think about scaling. Let's call this the "minimum lovable prototype."

If you see that the users don't trust the solution or do not see the value and you are having to try to convince them to use it, you need to step back, take their feedback, and see how you can improve your solution. Maybe you need to stay in the piloting phase longer, or even go back to the drawing board and start again from the prototyping phase.

Having said that, I have an exception for scaling your solution before you have the minimum lovable prototype. This is when you want to roll out an AI solution to collect high-quality data because you don't have it at the beginning of the project. In other words, you are scaling your AI solution to capture quality data.

Let me explain. Let's say you want to create an AI solution to inspect how well or badly your welders perform their job. To do that, imagine you need to prepare 10,000 examples of good and bad welds. At the beginning of the project, you may not have a dataset of bad welds. (Who keeps a dataset of bad welds anyway?) What you can do in this case is use the limited number of welding photos you have, or algorithmically generate welding photos (i.e., the synthetic data discussed in Chapter 4) to train a machine learning model, knowing that the results will not be good. Then you can scale it across your projects for the purpose of collecting real weld photos. When your welders finish a weld, they take photos and send them via the app to your inspectors, who label the photos based on how good or bad they are. Over time, you can replace the algorithmically generated data with the real project data you receive to retrain your machine learning model and improve the accuracy.

You need to ensure that you have a minimum lovable prototype before scaling your solution.

To summarize: in the Innovate phase, you tested your solution in real projects. You worked with your end user to gather feedback on what is or is not working and how to improve your solution. Then you worked with your execution team to prioritize and decide how the solution should be improved. Then you measured the assumptions that you made in calculating the business viability of your solution, before finally preparing your solution for scale.

Augment

In this phase, your AI solution is deployed and being adopted by the end user inside or outside of your organization (see Figure 8-5). The successful adoption of an AI solution needs time, focus, and the support of your executives. After all, by introducing your AI solution you are probably changing the way your people work, and you need to have a plan and an execution strategy for how they should adopt the new solution. One strategy could be showing them how the AI solution makes their work easier and more enjoyable to do, and asking them to try it for a short period of time to see it for themselves. Nick Bagatelos, who was the president of Bagatelos Architectural Glass for more than three decades, shared with me his experience of bringing new innovative solutions to his company:

> *"One of your biggest challenges is getting buy-in from your staff. To do that, you should take an incremental approach by which you need to find value propositions that will show improvement to their workflow. Then ask them to try it to see how your AI solution reduces their time doing tedious tasks and allows them to do what they love. Once they see the value, they will take over and use the solution."*

After the successful adoption of your solution, you can reap the benefit of applying this technology to your core product offering and services, to your sales and marketing, and to the back end of your business to reduce pressure and increase productivity and profit margin.

This is a perfect time to look back and document what you've learned. It's also a good time to validate the hypotheses and assumptions you had at the beginning of the project. How difficult was running the project? What was the actual cost of the project? Are you on target to achieve your ROI? To do this, you can use the "Execute and document your AI journey" in the accompanying workbook.

Activity 8: Complete "Execute and document your AI journey" in the workbook.

The good thing is that you started from guesswork, and now you have actual data for running future projects.

Running your first AI project is like sending a rocket to the Moon: it requires a lot of initial time investment and over-engineering. In the beginning, your rocket consumes a lot of fuel but does not move too much, so you need to put a lot of energy into making it take off. But in the next project it gets better, and by the time you are on your third project, you'll feel that your rocket is moving on its own with no more energy required.

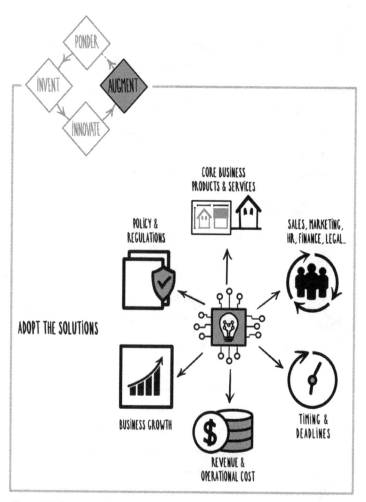

Figure 8-5: Augment phase

KEY TAKEAWAYS

- One of the important decisions you should make is whether to find an AI partner or create your own in-house AI team.
- To execute your AI project, you need to form your AI execution team and cross the knowledge chasm before starting the Invent phase.
- You should cross the knowledge chasm by onboarding and teaching your execution team about your problem and workflows, and learning from them about AI.
- The main goal of the prototyping phase is ideating, building solutions, and testing to validate the technical feasibility of the prototype you make.
- The main goal of the piloting phase is testing the prototype in real-world projects, improving the solution, and measuring the business viability of the prototype.
- Once you have a minimum lovable prototype, your solution is ready to scale. In some projects, however, scaling is the best way of capturing high-quality data, and must be done before reaching the scaling point.
- You can reduce pressure, increase productivity, and improve profit margin when your AI solution is in the Augment phase.
- You should document what worked, what didn't work, and why, and validate the assumptions and hypotheses you had when planning or executing the project.

EXPERIMENT TO LEARN

Jit Kee Chin is the chief data and innovation officer in Suffolk, a $4 billion general contractor in the US. Suffolk's vision is to integrate the entire building life cycle into a seamless platform to redefine how the world builds.

Jit Kee's team has been working on testing different use cases for AI within construction, then working with the business to scale those with an impact. Below, she shares an example of how they are developing an AI solution to enhance their safety program:

We are proud of our safety program at Suffolk. It promotes a safety culture that encourages workers to take action when they see safe or unsafe conditions. To further enhance this program, we experimented with using past data and AI to predict site safety risks. Before we started this experiment, we knew that it might not work, but we wanted to give it a shot and try.

In the beginning, we had some challenges with data. For instance, our data was in different systems that were not interoperable. The data quality was poor because some fields were left blank, and others had uncontrolled values. And the processes for capturing the data were not standardized. We've come a long way since then, when we became a data-aware company.

To do the project, we partnered with a technology provider. After onboarding them and sharing our processes and data, they created a proof-of-concept and prototype we could test in the lab environment. After some rounds of ideating solutions, building and improving the prototype, and measuring and testing it in the lab, we took the prototype to the piloting phase, where we faced some challenges.

The first challenge was the choice of the AI algorithm, which was based on statistical analysis techniques that look at past project data to make future predictions. But predictions are never 100% accurate – some predictions will be wrong, and that risks undermining the legitimacy of the entire algorithm, even if it is more often right than not. Another limitation of the AI solution was that it may not be able to fully explain the logic behind the results provided, as algorithmic techniques are complex and not intuitive.

Another challenge is the legal and liability implications of prediction. If the AI solution suggests that something will happen on the site today, but it does not, what happens? More importantly, if it predicts that something *will* happen, but the user does not take any action and an incident actually occurs, then is there a liability implication?

This challenge was echoed by the feedback we received from the construction experts. One of our safety managers asked, 'How can you tell me there is a high risk of accidents on site if you cannot tell me exactly who is going to get hurt and at what time and location? In this case, I don't know what set of actions I must take to mitigate the risk.' Another question was, 'Who is liable when the AI solution is wrong, or if the safety managers neglect the recommended results?'

In summary, I think many of our industry's challenges with using predictive AI come down to thinking through how we operationalize it. What are the actions we will take given a prediction? How do we think about the risk? How will our project teams handle the predictions? We have not yet scaled our AI solution because some of these questions are unanswered. But the experience that we gained out of the safety experimentation was invaluable. It allowed us to get our data in shape and look at it in a way we've not looked at it before.

My recommendation to other AEC executives and business

leaders is to start experimenting with AI now. It exposes you to what you don't know and points the way forward for what you need to do. If some of your experiments do not work, understand the reason, learn from it, and take those learnings to your next experiment.

CHAPTER 9

Define your AI strategy

One weekend when I was in San Francisco, I decided to go to a meet-up called Dragon Boat at Berkeley Marina. I arrived at 8:00 a.m. and saw more than thirty other people wearing the same yellow and black outfits, as if they were part of the same team. They looked like professionals. Later, someone told me that they would be racing in two weeks; that's why they put all the newbies like me on the same boat for that day.

After going over some instructions and safety procedures, our boat captain showed up and welcomed us. All fifteen newbies circled around him to listen while he explained the rowing procedure and how we needed to row in harmony. I was excited, and I could see the excitement on other people's faces.

When we got into the boat, the coach said, "Today, our boat is going to help the main team prepare for their race." In other words, we had to race with them. It seemed impossible! Then, the coach explained different strategies that we could use. "We divide the race into three parts: start strong, sustain, and all-out. And to do that, you should listen carefully to my drum, which is the cue for your paddle position. Any time you hear it, your paddle should be in front of you, on the water, just before you initiate your pull. To show you how important listening to the drum is, I want you to paddle for a mile without my cues."

I thought to myself, how hard could it be? He explained everything to us, so we should be able to paddle easily. I was wrong. My paddle was constantly hitting the paddle of the person in front and in back. Everyone had their own interpretation of what harmony was. It was mayhem. We put lots of energy into rowing, but the boat did not go that far. It felt like we were going two steps forward and one step back. We were highly inefficient, and everyone was soon exhausted.

By contrast, when the coach started to give the signal, everything changed. All of a sudden, we got into the same rowing pattern as if we were one unit. We fell into harmony by following the coach's leads and instructions. We were using less energy this time, and the boat was going a lot faster. After an hour of practicing different rowing patterns, we put the coach's strategy into action. We started strong, sustained our energy and efforts in the middle section of the race, and sprinted for the last third. The result? We didn't win, but we did our best. And that, for me, was a success. It was amazing to see how a true leader can get the best out of a team by defining a clear strategy and the steps to take to make it real.

That day is gone, but the lesson I learned stayed with me. Imagine your company is a boat, and every department in your company is a person with a paddle. Without cuing your employees, everyone paddles in a particular direction, but one that makes sense to them. In your company, the decisions you make across the organization about data and AI projects may conflict with the decisions that others make to run their own projects. For instance, you might want project data to be named and tagged in a certain way so that you can use it in future projects to train a machine learning model, but the project team wants to name it differently because that's the way they have done it for many years.

You need to create and execute a blueprint that guides your employees' decisions so that everybody paddles in the same direction. That blueprint is your AI strategy.

Without an AI strategy, every department will make inconsistent and ad hoc decisions that limit your company's effectiveness in achieving your AI vision.

You might think that you should always set a strategy first and then define supporting projects; so, why do you set an AI strategy *after* you have done your first AI project? The reason is that AI is relatively new, and you first need to learn about and experiment with it in a quick-win project, as explained in the previous chapters. Once you better understand its capabilities by going through the four phases of the AI augmentation framework, you can establish your AI strategy and various projects to support it.

In this chapter, you'll learn how to establish an AI strategy for your company. But first, what is an AI strategy?

What is an AI strategy?

An AI strategy is a plan of action that guides you and other managers in your company to make consistent decisions to achieve key AI objectives. It aligns the efforts of all players in your organization to move in one direction, taking into account the resources you have.

The starting point for establishing your AI strategy is your business strategy. Perhaps you are entering a new market in certain areas (offense strategy) or want to defend or sustain your market position in other areas. To connect strategies from different business areas to your AI strategy, you can use the AI augmentation framework discussed in Chapter 7. Previously, you used the framework to define your first AI project; now, you can use it to determine several AI projects across your company that expand your capabilities on a larger scale.

To do that, using your business strategies, you need to find and prioritize AI use cases using either existing business problems or problems identified by the SOAR framework. For instance, in Figure 9-1 you can see that there are three AI use cases: two coming from the SOAR framework, and one from existing business problems. Therefore, in the Invent phase, you will have multiple AI projects grouped and labeled as AI initiatives (e.g., the six AI projects and three AI initiatives in Figure 9-1). Each AI initiative serves one of the business goals of your company. For example, with the business goal of increasing sales by 10%, you can define an AI initiative and several AI projects to support it.

Not all your AI prototypes will pass the technical feasibility stage and go to the Innovate phase (e.g., in Figure 9-1 only two prototypes from the Invent phase went to the Innovate phase). With enough resources you can pilot a few solutions simultaneously, but when it gets to the scaling stage I highly recommend proceeding with one solution at a time. As discussed before, the adoption of your AI solution takes considerable time and energy, because you are disrupting the way your organization and employees usually work. So, focus on one project at a time to make sure you can get benefit from your solution in the Augment phase.

Now that you have learned how the AI augmentation framework can help you escalate your AI endeavor, I'd like to explain why having and documenting an AI strategy is important. Most AEC companies have various lines of business, and are playing offense, defense, and sustain in different markets and regions at the same time. In Chapter 7, you learned that the speed of AI project execution differs depending on whether you are employing the defense or the offense strategy. Therefore, you'll find yourself running multiple projects with different timelines and goals. So, it is critical to define a strategy and document it to make it clear to yourself and to all the stakeholders and sponsors involved.

But how do you define an AI strategy for your company?

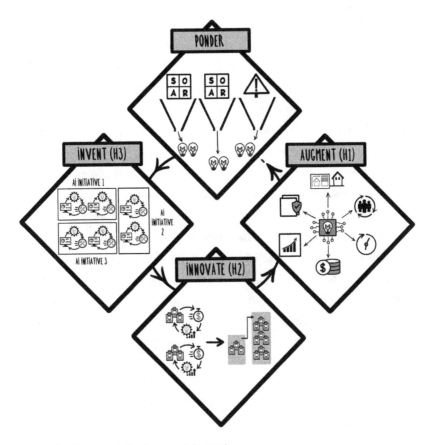

Figure 9-1: AI augmentation framework in practice

Four components of your AI strategy

To define your AI strategy, use the AI augmentation framework and your business strategy to define its four components:

1. AI vision (*Why*)
2. Business objectives and outcomes (*What*)
3. AI initiatives and projects (*How*)
4. Connection to data strategy (*How*)

Let's look at each in detail.

1. AI vision (Why)

Marta, who had joined a construction company a month ago, was working really hard in her home office late one evening. Her husband, Sam, knocked on the door and came in. He stood by her side, wondering when she was going to stop working. He cleared his throat and asked, "I noticed your new job is really demanding. I've never seen you working this hard! You know your health is important, right?" Marta looked at him and said, "My health, *and* the health of 5,000 employees on the site. I'm trying to make the construction site accident-free. Can you imagine how crucial it is to the 5,000 families of these people?" Marta is not a safety manager or superintendent: she is a graphics designer, and on this night she was labeling construction safety photos taken from the site so that AI engineers can create an app for intelligent safety monitoring and control on site, with the ambitious goal of making construction sites accident-free. She could see a clear connection between her work and the AI vision of her company.

Without a vision, you won't have highly motivated and firmly committed employees to achieve the set objectives. And without their engagement, you cannot succeed in aligning efforts inside your organization.

Your AI vision is a lofty and ambitious goal that you want to achieve. It is an internal compass and driving force for your departments and employees. This is the purpose behind your efforts, and describes the desired long-term results that you hope to achieve.

There is no single formula to define your AI vision. But remember, whatever you come up with should inspire other people to come and work for you. Here are some tips that you can use to define your AI vision:

- **Start with why.** In his book *Start With Why* and his TED Talk "How great leaders inspire action," Simon Sinek explains, "There are leaders, and there are those who lead. Leaders hold a portion of power or authority, but those who lead inspire us. Whether they are individuals or organizations, we follow those who lead not because we have to, but because we want to. And those who start with 'Why' have the ability to inspire those around them or find others who inspire them." So ask yourself: what is your cause, what's your purpose? Why should anyone care?
- **Think big, think ahead.** You don't want to set a vision that could be easily achieved in a year: you should think five to ten years ahead when setting your vision, and this is hard. "Most people overestimate what they can do in one year and underestimate what they can do in ten years," says Bill Gates. So, think about three to five years from now – what is the ambitious goal that you want to achieve by then?
- **Be brave.** You are developing an AI vision for your company. It's okay to think outside the box and develop a vision that could potentially disrupt your company or change your business model.

Key questions to discuss with your team:

- What is your cause, your purpose? And why should anyone care?
- What is a significant and audacious goal that you want to achieve five to ten years from now?
- How can you disrupt yourself before anyone else does?

2. Business objectives and outcomes (What)

Your business objective is what you want your team to achieve. Without a business objective that is aligned with your AI vision, your team will not know how how what they do relates to the company's bigger goal.

Without the top-down objectives and expected outcomes, you cannot align your teams, focus and commit to priorities, track for accountability, and get the full benefit from your AI investment.

In his book *Measure What Matters,* John Doerr recommends some of the best practices for defining business objectives and outcomes. I have summarized some of them here:

- **Avoid low-value objectives.** You should have objectives that matter to your customers, your teams, or your company. To find them, imagine that you have achieved your objective and ask yourself, "So what?" If there is no compelling answer, get rid of that objective.
- **Focus.** If you have a small AI team (less than four people), you may want to start with having one objective. The more objectives you have, the more people you need to execute them. You want your team to focus on delivering one objective rather than stretching very thin to deliver several objectives.
- **Include measurable results or business outcomes.** When writing the expected outcomes, make sure that they are measurable. For instance, instead of "conducting research" as an outcome, you should aim to "read twenty research papers by August 18."

Key questions to discuss with your team:

- What are your top three business goals?
- How is your AI vision aligned with your business goals?
- How significant are these goals when they are achieved?
- Is your expected outcome simple and measurable?

- How does your expected outcome contribute to achieving the objective?

3. AI initiatives (How)

In Chapter 8, you learned about running an AI project. In this chapter, we will call the one or multiple AI projects that you embark upon to support your objectives and expected results an *AI initiative*. Each initiative should focus on one objective and one or multiple business outcomes that the initiative has. In other words, an AI initiative is a collection of AI projects that support the same business objective. Without these projects and initiatives, you cannot achieve the objectives that you set. So, it is essential to define and execute these projects according to your AI vision, objective, and expected outcomes.

Let me share an example with you. Let's say one of your business objectives is to reduce the time of drawing production by 50%. The expected outcomes of this objective are generating building models in twenty-four hours and creating detail drawings in twelve hours.

- **Objective**: To reduce the time of drawing production by 50%
- **Expected outcome 1**: Generate ten building models in twenty-four hours
- **Expected outcome 2**: Create 100 detail drawings in twelve hours

Based on the above, you define an AI initiative called "intelligent drawing production", given this objective and two expected outcomes. Then, for each of the expected outcomes, you can specify one or multiple projects, as follows:

- **AI initiative**: Intelligent drawing production
- **Project 1**: Generate Revit models by sketch
- **Project 2**: Generate detail drawings using an intelligent reasoner

To execute each project, you should work with your AI team and go through the Invent, Innovate, and Augment phases, as explained in Chapter 8.

4. Connection to data strategy

How do your data strategy and governance support your AI projects to ultimately generate business values?

You learned about the 5 Vs of data and the importance of having data governance in Chapter 4, so I am not going to repeat that again here. The only point I'd like to make is that your data strategy and governance should be in line with your AI strategy. Without that alignment, you may not get access to the high-quality and structured data that is the main ingredient of your AI solutions.

People often think that having more data is better for creating AI solutions, but this is not the case: having more good-quality and structured data is better, *not* having more noisy and unstructured data. So, it is critical to make sure that your data strategy serves your AI projects.

You need to think about how you can increase the quality of your data to serve your AI projects at scale.

Activity 9: complete the "Document your AI strategy" in the workbook.

KEY TAKEAWAYS

- You must have an AI strategy that is connected to your business strategy.
- The four components of your AI strategy are AI vision (*Why*), business objectives and outcomes (*What*), AI initiatives and projects (*How*), and data strategy (*How*).
- Without an AI vision, you won't have highly motivated and firmly committed employees to achieve the set objectives.
- A business objective aligned with your AI vision helps your team know how what they do relates to the company's bigger goal.
- Each AI initiative or project must contribute to the business goal of the company.
- Your AI strategy must be aligned with the data strategy and governance of your company.

AI AUGMENTATION IS A JOURNEY

Alain Waha is the CTO of Buro Happold. In Chapter 1, you learned his point of view about climate change and why we need AI and technology to solve these problems.

As a CTO and technology leader, Alain has observed and contributed to many technologies over the past several years. Below, he shares his thoughts about the best practices and mindset of executing projects:

How do you make your company a place where top talents, data, and AI work together to create value and improve your customers' experience and, ultimately, the people of the planet? The short answer is by establishing a culture of innovation and starting your AI transformation journey.

If you are embarking on your AI journey, you should know that it starts with people – like any other journey. So it is essential, to begin with, to determine your purpose and your 'why'. Take a look at the purpose of your company's existence and work with your team on creating your AI vision and the reason why you want to do AI projects.

Unlike a regular journey, where you can set your destination before your journey starts, your AI journey does not have a predefined arrival point. AI is an exponential technology that can take your business to unexpected places. So, a deterministic AI strategy will not work. I don't think Amazon set out to make a cloud or AI business, or Apple knew that they would enter the music streaming business when they launched iPod. So, as an AEC executive and leader, you must create an environment for opportunities to emerge and then recognize them rather than deterministically trying to decide what they are.

It is also critical to not let your current business model block you and your team. For instance, Apple's business model was to sell iPods. If they ignored opportunities based on their business model at the time, they would have never acquired iTunes, or opened the iTunes stores, or got into the streaming business. None of this would have happened if they had constrained themselves to their business model at the time. So, have the right mindset by being open-minded.

After establishing your purpose and getting into the right mindset, you need to start your incubation or invention phase. Since you've just begun your AI journey, and perhaps your digital transformation journey, your company might be so immature that the business value of your AI experimentations may not be apparent. This is expected, because the actual value of the experimentation at the start of your AI journey is learning. So, fail fast, learn fast, iterate quickly, and have fun. After doing enough experiments, you'll understand how and when AI can propel your business.

It would be best not to expect to scale all your AI solutions before you need to or want to. After piloting and testing projects, if some of your solutions seem mature enough, you can consider bringing them into your core business to improve your business' productivity or operations side.

In that phase, one of the challenges you will find is the collision between the incumbent and insurgent within your business. The old part of your business acts as an incumbent and resists your solution, which behaves like an insurgent. In other words, you want to do something different, but some people want to keep doing what the business has been doing previously. That's why you need to have buy-in from the highest level of the organization – to smooth out this transformation.

Your AI journey will never end. Your AI experimentations help you understand the value of data and improve your data governance and strategy, taking you towards higher maturity levels. Based on your new level of maturity, you can take on new AI experiments and projects that you could not do before, which could help you become more mature. This cycle goes on and on. Have fun and stay curious.

Onward.

PART 4

AI in Practice

Up until now, this book has been designed to give you an education. I want you to learn about AI so that you can begin to use it. You have learned about what AI is, how to spot an AI use case with business value, how to run an AI project, and how to create a strategy for your company. When you begin to use AI in your business, you will continue to learn. AI is very much about experimentation and adaption. Nothing illustrates this better than an examination of how AI is being used today – now – in real-world settings.

So, in this part of the book, I'm going to change directions a little bit. Throughout the book we've been hearing from many people who are using AI in their business today, but now I want to go into more depth. I'm going to review, in detail, three case studies from some of the leading design and construction companies in the world.

To help you see how other companies develop AI solutions that augment their capabilities and give them competitive advantage in the market, I interviewed three thought leaders and distilled the essence of their projects. I also mapped their projects to some of the discussions that we have had in the book to help you see how the education you have had up to this point translates to a real business situation. As you read each case study, you'll learn how each company essentially used the four steps of the AI augmentation framework – Ponder, Invent,

Innovate, and Augment – in their projects. You'll also hear about the AI strategy that each company has developed following their experience with AI projects. I also asked these thought leaders to share any advice, in the form of recommendations, that they may have with people who have not run an AI project before. In other words, I don't want you to just take my word for it that AI is going to help you – I want you to hear it from people experimenting with and using it today.

Please note that most of these projects are ongoing, and they may change direction as they develop.

Augment creativity and design agility

Yoshito Tsuji is the general manager of the design department at Obayashi Corporation in Japan and Singapore, and is now leading Asia Digital Labs (ADL) in Singapore. He received his bachelor's and master's degrees in architecture from Kyoto University in 1988 and 1992, and his master's of architecture in urban design from Harvard University in 2002. He believes that designs of the future should be done in less time, but provide more in terms of environmental sustainability, a concept he calls the "Less and More" strategy. Over twenty-five years, he has completed various design-build projects – mainly offices, data centers, and commercial buildings – and is now focusing on digitalized design-build in Singapore through ADL's research.

I will now share Yoshito's AI journey, in his own words:

"When I joined Obayashi in 1996, most of the time our client was a single person – or if it was a company, we only dealt with the executives, such as the CEO, and a limited number of people. It was a time when the financial aspect of the project was not as critical as it is today. The laws and regulations were still strict then, but the requirements from clients were less difficult; they were usually simple to address.

"But today, the clients are more sophisticated. They are a group of people or stakeholders whose highest priority is the return on investment for their multinational investment funds. To get the expected return, they bring in a very large budget and want the project to be designed and built in a very short time. This short schedule brings a lot of pressure to the work we do. Besides the complexity of clients, the regulations on the environment and community have become more stringent, and the requirements of projects have become more complex. Therefore, architects are no longer able to reach a solution in a short time. In 2016, we had an 'aha' moment when we realized that it is beyond our capabilities to design and execute projects in such a short time.

"Our staff worked very hard and for long hours during the day, and even undertook overtime to meet client demands, but we could not keep up. Then our government set a maximum limit of forty-five overtime hours per month for employees. This rule made it impossible for us to reach our goals. Another challenge we have is that AEC professionals in Japan are reducing in numbers. As our senior managers are starting to retire, we need more young professionals to take management roles and learn how to plan, coordinate, and run projects. But there are not many young professionals coming to our profession. They would rather go to the tech industry or media and entertainment to become an influencer and make more money!

"So, we started looking into how AI can empower us to do more in fewer hours."

Let's now look at how Obayashi approached each phase of the AI augmentation framework.

The Ponder phase

"At the beginning of our AI project, we brainstormed various areas where AI could help our business to grow – from conceptual design development to detailed design and even the construction of projects. One of the opportunities we made it a priority to solve was getting client buy-in and building trust with them using the power of AI technology. Let me explain the problem in more detail.

"Our clients often have to make purchasing decisions on pieces of vacant commercial land, and they ask us to conduct a feasibility study for potential buildings. What we need to do is design the building volume and floor plans to calculate the rentable areas, and ultimately their return on investment. First, we discuss and document client requirements in a meeting at the client's office, then go back to our office to sketch a few options. One or two weeks later, we meet with the client to show them options and obtain their feedback. This repetitive process continues for several weeks until our client is satisfied.

"The AI use case for us was to be able to take in client requirements and generate design solutions for them in their office. In other words, we wanted to co-design with our clients in their office to get their buy-in and approval. That's why we started an AI experimentation: to remove lots of the inefficiencies in the design process and reduce the number of meaningless discussions.

"In addition to removing inefficiencies, one of our future goals is to use AI to bring sustainability and environmental aspects into our projects. Some of our clients only focus on the financial aspects of their project, ignoring the environmental and sustainability aspects. However, as a company, we want to serve our client and the sustainability needs of our planet, and the needs of our community. That's why we think AI can help us to find the balance and make better decisions that are in line with the needs of our community, the planet, and our customer. We hope to add these aspects into our future AI projects.

"The business viability was very obvious for us. If we spend a couple of million dollars in building a scalable solution, we can easily get a fivefold return at the end of the first year of using it. This was very much in line with our business strategy of sustaining innovation and continuing to innovate across the company. Since nobody had done what we wanted to do before, we assumed that it would be very difficult. Hence, technical feasibility was our biggest concern.

"So, in terms of the importance and difficulty of this opportunity, it was extremely important and very difficult to do. If I wanted to plot it on the importance/difficulty matrix, I would place it in the 'major strategic projects' quadrant."

The Invent phase

"To build our own AI solution, we started working with a technology partner to help us on our journey. To cross the knowledge chasm, we presented our problems in a multi-day workshop in our office. We showed how we design buildings, what the challenges are, and what our overall goal was for doing this AI experiment.

"Our technology partner took all the information and created various conceptual solutions for us. In terms of the branches of the AI tree, some concepts used machine learning, some used knowledge representation and reasoning, and some used optimization. We reviewed the conceptual solutions and provided feedback. We even used some of the concepts to create new concepts and workflows.

"Based on our feedback and the solution we prioritized, our technology partner instructed us on what type of data they needed and how they wanted data to be captured, formatted, and labeled. In the prototyping phase, our technology partner created a solution for co-design creation with clients."

The Innovate phase

"At the end of the experimentation, we piloted and tested the solution in one of our projects in Tokyo, and proved the efficiency and reliability of the new process. More testing and improvement still need to be done before scaling."

The Augment phase

"When scaled into our business, this AI solution can reduce our design time by at least 50%. Therefore, this solution can potentially save millions of dollars for Obayashi every year. Besides, it augments the capabilities of our designers by removing the tedious, repetitive, and counter-productive design tasks. Instead, they'll have more time to spend on the creative aspects of design."

Now that we've learned about how Obayashi approached their AI project, let's hear what Yoshito had to say about the challenges the company faced, before going on to the AI strategy that they developed.

"Two big challenges that we had in our project were a lack of data and the knowledge gap between our design team and our technology partner. In order to train a machine learning model, we needed to prepare a dataset of more than 2,000 buildings. Some of these projects had been done in the past and were in different databases. Or some of them were in old CAD format that should have been translated and labeled so it could be understood by the AI algorithm.

"Another challenge we had was communication. We want to have an AI agent that learns from our explicit design knowledge and the rules that we use in our design practice (e.g., rules of thumb to design building core, bathrooms, or an office layout). But as architects, we are not used to expressing what our design principles are. Documenting our design process, codifying our knowledge, and communicating our human intelligence to our technology partner was challenging, but worth it. We overcame this challenge by meeting regularly with our technology partner and educating them about our workflows and processes."

AI strategy

"Before starting this project, we had a vision and strategy. I'd say that completing this project and experimenting with building a solution helped us to make that strategy more realistic. One of the areas that we underestimated was the difficulty of preparing data and the time it takes to do that.

"But, having that experience under our belt, we now know what to do for the future."

AI vision

"We want to be a leading design and construction technology platform in the AEC industry. Our AI vision is to invent novel AI solutions that can augment the capabilities of our designers so that we can execute our projects faster and with increased quality."

Business objectives and outcomes

"From the business standpoint, we want to reduce the design time by 50%. This will enable us to save millions of dollars in operational costs and increase our revenue by winning more projects."

AI initiatives

"In this solution, we put in client requirements such as location, floor-to-area ratio, and adjacency requirements as the input. The machine learning agent, which is trained on our past data, takes these inputs and generates multiple building masses immediately. This is where we can sit with our client and present different building masses, get their feedback, and come up with what they want right away. But the process does not stop here.

"After selecting the building mass, we use another AI agent to assist us with the design of a floor plan. First, we choose a typical floor and select the type and number of units or rooms we should place in that floor. Next, using some of our design rules and defined principles, the AI agent places units on the floor. What we like about this process is the ability to show the client instantly whether we can satisfy their requests or not. For instance, they may ask to add five more conference rooms on a particular floor. Before using this tool, we had to go back to the office and spend a week coming up with a solution, but now we can immediately tell the client whether it works or not and how it looks. I see the role of AI as a translator or mediator between us and our clients. It helps us manage expectations, build trust with clients, and ultimately win more projects."

Data strategy

"Before doing this project, we thought we had enough projects and data to train a machine learning model. We spent almost a year on preparing more than 400 labeled BIM models. Then we used basic geometry operation, like rotation, translation, and scaling, to augment this data to almost 3,000 models. What we learned was that because of the complexity of the problem, the machine learning algorithm needed around 100,000 data points, which we did not have. So, our technology partner used parametric modeling tools to create our database (synthetic data generation). We thought we had a lot of data, but it was not enough!

"Another learning from the project was in the area of data governance. When you have more than two people creating data or labeling your dataset, you must have a framework on how data should be prepared and labeled. One person may label a space as 'washing room,' another person as 'bathroom' or 'WC.' It may sound really simple, but if you ignore this step, your AI project will fail.

"Bringing our learning from this AI experimentation, we now have bigger plans and a strategy for how to capture, store, and label data across our organization and company. I'm very glad that we took this learning from this project because, without it, we could have continued storing data for years without thinking about its quality."

Recommendations

Find the right technology partner

"Some people think that their AI partner should be expert in the problem that they have. But I found the opposite to be true. My advice to people who want to start their first AI experimentation is to find a technology partner that has a different expertise, point of view, and way of thinking from yours. It was possible for us to hire some people internally and kick off our project, but we found a technology partner that could bring in a new way of solving our problems that we could not have done alone."

A good AI solution is your advisor and partner in solving problems

"You need to understand that we are dealing with narrow AI today, which has very limited capabilities. But it doesn't have to stop us from using it. The narrow AI is great for automating mundane tasks, which will enable us to work on the more creative part of our job. For instance, in our project we codified our knowledge in the form of sentences and rules into the AI agent, and we gained new knowledge from the AI agent through how it is performing some of our tasks efficiently. I'm really excited about the symbiotic relationship between the AI and human, where designers can focus on the more creative side of design, AI focuses on automating tasks that take time, and we both learn from each other along the way."

Be adaptable

"The pace of change and technology adoption is very low in our industry. My recommendation to our executives is that once you have created an AI solution, or even before then, you need to think about how it will impact your processes and how you can prepare your workforce for that. A lot of the time people develop technologies and get excited by trying something new, but after a while they go back to the old way of doing things. So, be flexible and lead the change inside your organization to augment your capabilities."

This is just the beginning

"Once you have done some experimentation and have a proof-of-concept or have implemented a solution, you are at the beginning of a bigger journey. You need to frequently train your AI agents to keep up with all the trends happening in the market. So it's not like you trained it once and you're done – it's an ongoing process, because the trend in design is always changing. It has been changing for many years. Our built environment is changing, and so is the AI."

Augment sales and business growth

Gilles Caussade has been working in small and large construction companies in multiple continents and countries for more than twenty-five years. He used to plan and execute multibillion-dollar projects, mainly in the oil and gas and energy sectors, before joining ConXtech as the CEO.

ConXtech is changing how we design and build structures by introducing a novel technology called "collar," which is used for connecting steel beams to columns. Using this technology, and with a limited number of steel beams and column sections, the company can build small and large structures in a fraction of the time when compared to conventional steel structures. For instance, they erected the structure of a 230,000-square-foot (21,367-square-meter) data center in fifteen days!

After completing an AI project, Gilles believes that AI technology can help ConXtech to grow exponentially. Here is what Gilles had to say:

The Ponder phase

"Our AI journey started when I realized that we had a big bottleneck in the growth of our company. Over the next several years, our strategy is to grow. To do that, we need to invest up front in activities associated with our company's sales and business development. We discovered an AI use case by looking at our strategy to grow, and trying to remove the bottleneck in the process.

"Our big question was how to enable our sales team to grow revenue tenfold while keeping the overhead low and almost constant. We had a hunch that AI might help, but we didn't know precisely how.

"Let me explain the details of the problem and the bottleneck in the sales process.

"To increase sales, we need to bid on more projects. Our typical bidding process starts with receiving a request for a quotation. At that point our structural engineering team, which is in the service of our sales team, is engaged to design the building with our kit-of-parts (i.e., a limited number of beams and columns, and specialized connections known as collar). They spend days and sometimes weeks making sure that the building is structurally safe, serviceable, and complies with building codes. Some buildings are not compatible, and therefore all the time that engineers spend goes to waste. We create a bill of materials for those buildings that are compatible and run cost estimations to calculate the bid price. So it's a long, repetitive, tedious, and costly process.

"Because of our industry's meager win ratio (typically 10% to 20%) and the extremely long cycle of the projects (typically three to five years), we need to spend a lot of money up front before we receive the benefit. In other words, it takes three to five years to get a return on 20% of the projects that we bid on.

"Another significant expense for us is hiring very experienced designers and engineers to help the sales team win projects. That team includes certified engineers, 3D modelers, quantity take-off experts, estimators, and experienced construction managers. The more we want to grow, the more we need to hire these people to help the sales team. We need to build a group of people who know our product very well and are extremely expensive. Outsourcing is too risky and not an option for us.

"Because of the ups and downs of the market, this group of experts is either overloaded and overwhelmed by the amount of work, or they have nothing to do. It might be possible to find some people to do that for one or two years, but after that they will leave. This means that turnover is generated very quickly, which creates recruiting problems. We spend money on recruiting, training, and developing talent, but unfortunately we cannot retain our talent for more than two years.

"All things considered, it's an almost impossible equation for growth.

"In terms of business viability, I'd say that this use case can bring more than a tenfold return on investment when we solve this problem. Investing in AI has some upfront costs, but will produce a considerable return after just two or so years. In terms of feasibility, at the beginning I thought it was impossible, but our technology partner proved that it could be done.

"So, this project was extremely important and very difficult to do. If I wanted to plot it on the importance/difficulty matrix, I would place it firmly in the 'major strategic projects' quadrant.

"To solve this problem, we partnered up with an AI technology provider."

The Invent phase

"To cross the knowledge chasm, we met frequently to educate our AI technology provider about ConXtech's process and workflows. The most challenging part of our partnership was at the beginning, when we exchanged information. That knowledge transfer has its learning curve, and it took time for them to learn our process. Similarly, it took us some time to understand AI technology. We came from two different worlds with two different languages, but, after a few meetings, we could understand each other.

"To onboard the team rapidly, we invited them to come to our company to spend time with our engineers and project managers, and visit our fabrication facilities. Some team members worked with and shadowed our sales, engineering, and estimating teams to learn more about our processes.

"Once our AI technology provider understood our process well, they came up with various concept posters and ideas about how to solve the problem. Based on our feedback, they refined their concepts. After multiple reviews, we selected the concept that was related to automating our whole front-end process. At that point, I thought to myself that it would be impossible to achieve. But at the end of the Invent phase, we had an AI technology prototype that used data to design and optimize buildings for cost and serviceability."

The Innovate phase

"In the Innovate phase, we piloted and tested the prototype on one of our projects. The AI solution could create lots of designs and evaluate them in a couple of hours, compared to the usual days and weeks. We were able to say quickly whether a particular project was a go or no-go, and present the best design and cost. So, what used to take weeks can now take a few hours. Now, the impossible is possible."

The Augment phase

"AI allows us to reduce or keep the company's overheads constant, even when growing. When using the AI engine in the sales division of our business, the bidding process is no longer a bottleneck. The AI agent is accurate and easy to use, and that will allow me to grow the business and the value of this company for investors and stakeholders."

AI strategy

"This project was our first experimentation with AI, and I'm incredibly pleased with the outcome and the learnings that came out of it. My AI strategy for the company is straightforward: once I secure enough capital for the project, I'll invest in developing and rolling out the AI technology inside ConXtech and, more importantly, the design and engineering community in the US and worldwide. This way, when an architect or structural engineer is working on a building they can get quick feedback on their design with the ConXtech technology [Level 2]. This is how we get tremendous leverage. Instead of limiting this AI tool to internal use, we can enable thousands of designers and engineers to bring ConXtech technology into their solutions. This can accelerate market penetration, brand recognition, and the company's growth, and, as a result, increase technology adoption across the construction industry."

Recommendations

Be curious and open-minded

"AI is a generic technology that can make impossible things possible, but we are not wired to think about the impossible. That's why you need to reset your thinking and expectations when running your first AI project."

Embrace the serendipity

"Planning and executing an AI project is not like other technology projects. Sometimes we call software development companies to talk about specific problems, and ask them for a proposal by the end of the week. I read the proposal, and two weeks or a month later, the issue is resolved. Your AI project won't be like this. You need to step back and take time to explore opportunities, and sometimes you may need to reconsider what your problem is. You must come with that mindset, or your project is not going to work."

Expect the unexpected

"When I started working with our AI technology provider, I had some expectations. But as I learned more about AI and what it can do, I've evolved. My expectations and goals have completely changed for the better. I saw how the impossible could become possible if we trust each other and take some time to understand each other's worlds. It has been a journey. If you're not ready for the journey, don't take it. But if you are, it's going to change your mind, your business, and our world for the better."

Augment inspection and quality control

Hamzah Shanbari is the director of innovation at The Haskell Company, a design and construction company based in Jacksonville, Florida. He holds a PhD in design, construction, and planning from the University of Florida, and has more than eighteen years of experience in research and development of novel solutions for the AEC industry. In his current work, he oversees the technology and innovation strategy and implementation for his company.

Here is a summary of the discussion that I had with Hamzah:

"Back in 2018, our new CEO started several new strategic initiatives to change the way we have been doing things. He set goals for the company and identified where we wanted to be in five to ten years. One of the areas that he identified was innovation: 'We want to be at the forefront of technology and lead the industry in design and construction technology,' he said. To do that, we created an R&D group with full-time staff, and a dedicated budget and resources."

The Ponder phase

"Even though our R&D group has managers and directors with diverse backgrounds – in construction modeling and sequencing, IoT, finance, and even machine learning – we didn't want to just pick an idea and execute it.

"We believe that the best ideas and opportunities come from the people in the field. So, we tried to build a culture of entrepreneurship and innovation at Haskell. We used the vision and goals that our executives set for our company and asked all employees to propose solutions on how we might achieve them. We even held a Shark Tank-style event called 'Big Pitch,' where we invited people in the company to pitch ideas, and get funded and awarded.

"An idea was presented to us by one of our weld inspectors, Gary, who has more than forty years of experience in inspection and welding. In his presentation, he said, 'I don't know much about the technology, but I know that these days I can take photos with my phone and access my emails on the site. What if I take a photo of a weld and my phone tells me if it's a good weld or not?'

"We decided to fund Gary's idea, and this is the AI project that I want to share with you. But first, let me explain exactly what the problem is, and why this project was funded.

"We build a lot of manufacturing facilities and distribution warehouses for the food and beverage industry. In these facilities, we must build miles of stainless steel pipes which carry the main products of the factory, such as the wine, milk, and yogurt that we consume every day. These pipes are two or three inches in diameter, and twenty-five to thirty-five feet in length when we purchase and ship them to site.

"To build a one-mile pipe, a certified welder needs to weld many shorter pipes together. Because our food goes into these pipes, the weld that connects two pipes must be clean and precise. The quality of these welds depends on the experience of the welders, and we have a mix of experienced and less experienced welders on each project. Besides the skill of welding, the quality of welding can also be impacted by how tired workers are: they work from 6:00 a.m. to 6:00 p.m., and can be tired when they get to the end of their shift.

"To make sure that these welds are of the highest quality, we have a team of certified weld inspectors. These very highly paid inspectors go to the sites and visually inspect each weld. The challenge is that we have thousands of welds in each project and hundreds of projects spread out geographically, but only two certified weld inspectors. So, the ratio of the quantity of welding that needs be inspected to the number of inspectors is overwhelmingly high. And for us, it wouldn't make sense to hire too many certified weld inspectors, because they are highly paid professionals.

"Because the inspectors cannot be everywhere at the same time, every now and then the superintendent calls them to visit a site and inspect the welds. They are on call, and reactive rather than proactive.

"The consequence of delivering a project with a bad weld could be significant. A bad weld should be fixed if a manufacturer finds one – both after we deliver a project and during the facility's operation. However, fixing such welds under warranty would require shutting down operations, which could lead to loss of revenue. This is how important the welding is for these facilities. It has never happened to us, and, hopefully, won't ever happen.

"In terms of business viability, we calculated the return on investment for this project. Two factors that we considered in calculating the ROI were time and cost of the travel for our certified welding inspectors. On average, one inspector travels sixty times a year and each trip can take from one day to a week, depending on the complexity of the project. Considering the hourly rate of $200 and the cost of flights, accommodation, food and beverages, and so forth, it's possible to spend $1 million to $2 million a year on welding inspections. If we can cut our inspection expenses by half, we have a number that is five times more than the planned investment in our AI solution. We could have added the cost of potential rework and so on, but for simplicity we decided not to.

"In terms of technical feasibility, we initially thought it would be easy to create a solution. We had seen some companies and start-ups working on concrete-crack inspections, and thought there were some similar solutions out there. This led us to believe that finding a solution would not be too difficult.

"In terms of the importance and difficulty of this opportunity, it was extremely important and less difficult to do. I would put it in the 'quick wins' quadrant, if I wanted to plot it on the importance/difficulty matrix.

"To build the solution, we initially started capturing data and trying to train our own machine learning model. We wanted to experiment and learn from our successes and failures. We used some off-the-shelf libraries and trained a machine learning model, but it did not perform as we expected. This experimentation helped us to have a better understanding of the field, and know what type of questions we should ask when working with a technology partner."

The Invent phase

"In terms of crossing the knowledge chasm, we had a communication challenge in onboarding the researchers from the technology partner. The people who were doing the machine learning research and development do not know anything about welding. We had to sit down with our certified inspector multiple times to teach them what a good versus a bad weld is. They need to know this to measure the accuracy of the model trained, so we spent a lot of time educating them.

"Next, we came up with different AI concepts. One conceptual idea was to develop an app for welders. Imagine [that] when a welder completes a weld, he or she can take photos from different sides of the pipe, and the app can instantly give them feedback on how good or bad the welding is.

"Another idea that we pursued was to build an app for our certified inspectors who are not on the site. In this case, when a welder takes photos of the welding, the photos will be classified into good or bad welds using our machine learning model. The certified inspector can verify the welds that have deficiencies, then send a superintendent to the location of the weld for detailed inspections with an X-ray machine. In this scenario, the inspector can analyze all the welding from all active projects from his office.

"When we went to the prototyping phase, we realized that we had a challenge. We didn't have a clean, organized, and labeled dataset. In the first phase of the project, we wanted to have an AI prototype that could tell us what type of welding was shown in a photograph and identify any deficiencies that exist. To prepare the dataset, we needed to have hundreds of photos of both high-quality and deficient welds. To address this deficiency, we went to a construction site and asked our welders to make some good and bad welds. We took as many photos as possible from different angles and in different lighting to create our dataset."

The Innovate phase

"We are piloting and testing this AI engine in one of our projects and providing feedback from the field to the AI developers. I'm very excited to see how we can roll it out in our company and reap the benefits of AI at scale."

The Augment phase

"We, as humans, are confined in physical spaces, but artificial intelligence is not. It is scalable across projects and geographies. When this project is scaled, it will augment our inspectors' capabilities and help us improve our quality control process in a significant way. It can save us millions of dollars every year, and, even better, provide us with ease and peace of mind because every weld is checked and virtually certified."

AI strategy

AI vision

"We want to be a construction technology leader in the industry. We believe that AI has the potential to augment our workforce and scale our operation, especially in inspection and quality control."

Business objectives and outcomes

"We want to reduce the time and cost of welding inspections; we want to ensure we have a consistent documentation of all the welds in our job sites. Today, we are not documenting all the welds.

"Knowing that every weld that our trade partners are executing on the job site is documented gives us peace of mind. If there is a lawsuit in the future, you have all the documents to prove that it was not your fault, and you did your job the way you are supposed to."

AI initiatives

"In the conventional process, inspection is ad hoc and requires a lot of judgment calls by non-certified inspectors. They walk the site and randomly look at welds, and when they find a questionable weld they may call a certified inspector.

"It is impossible for our two certified inspectors to be present at all construction locations all the time. That's why they wait to receive calls from superintendents when things go wrong on the site. Their inspection process is manual, and relies on climbing ladders and using other equipment to do the inspection.

"In the AI-enabled process, once the welding of two pipes is completed, the welder takes several photos of the weld from all the different sides and around the pipe and tags them. While it is possible for the AI agent to provide instant feedback on the quality of welding, all the photos are sent to our AI agent for categorizing based on their quality. Our certified inspectors receive a copy of low-quality welds that our AI engine flagged for further review and assessment.

"This AI agent serves as a semi-certified weld inspector in the hands of all of our welders."

Data strategy

"AEC companies often think that they have lots of data, and they do. We have lots of weld photos, but they are unstructured, disorganized, and scattered in different databases. When we set our intention of what we wanted to do with them, we realized we have lots of gaps in our data. So, we had to go back to square one to start capturing data in a different way.

"I'm excited about this project, because now we know exactly how to systematically capture and label data in our company for weld inspection purposes. From now on, every weld in our project is a data point for the future, and every welder is a data collector.

"We have a strategy and system in place to become a construction data company in the near future."

Recommendations

Experiment, but seek help from pros

"Going back to the experimentation that we have done internally, we initially thought that we could do this on our own and didn't need anybody else. But soon, we got to a point where we were just spinning our wheels. Doing machine learning research is both art and science; it is a lot more than labeling something and sending it to the cloud to wait and see what happens. What I would recommend is to find somebody that has done that before and can get you to where you need to be. You should work with them and learn from them instead of doing it on your own, at least for your first AI project."

Have the end game in mind before you start

"I have another piece of advice about the AI use case. A lot of companies think about how AI can help them, but they don't do it in a strategic way. You need to be very clear about the business goals and desired outcome before even starting a project. Write down all your metrics for success so that you can measure against them at the end of the project."

Educate yourself

"A lot of people that we talked to, especially in the construction industry, think about AI as something futuristic: they say that 'It doesn't apply to what I'm doing.' My advice is to stop this way of thinking and start learning more about this technology. Read a book, take a course, and educate yourself. The fear of

AI arises when people don't have enough knowledge and are not educated about the topic."

Do more with less

"The other fear that people have is that we're taking away their jobs, but we're not. What we are doing is getting rid of inefficient parts of the job so that each person can do a lot more with less. There are big opportunities out there, and you should take advantage of AI to automate and optimize tasks, and make better decisions. I believe that we can do better as an industry."

Now that you have heard from three AEC professionals making real progress with AI in their respective businesses, I hope that you feel even more confident about experimenting with AI in your own business. I also hope that you understand how crucial it is to keep an open mind and be adaptable and agile as your journey with AI continues. It is a brave new world out there, one that I fear AEC professionals may be reluctant to join. But with the education provided by this book, and with these insights into current, real-world AI experimentation, I hope that you agree it is time to take the leap into a more productive, sustainable, and viable future – one made possible by the wonderful world of AI.

FINAL WORDS

This brings us to the end of our journey together – a journey of discovery. I wrote this book because I believe that AI is being underutilized in the AEC industry. One of the reasons that it is being underutilized is that AEC professionals don't know enough about it to know where and how to start using it. And when they try to educate themselves, as Tom did in the very first anecdote I told in the introduction, they can be overwhelmed by the amount of information out there. That's why, in this book, I have tried to give you the information and education you need to overcome your apprehension and confusion about AI, which in turn will encourage you to continue learning about it and finding ways to implement AI in your business.

In Part 1, you learned what AI is. We discussed the 5 Vs of data and how it can bring value to your company. After learning about biases, interactions, and the limitations of AI systems, you reviewed three examples of AEC AI systems in use today – in energy simulation, prefabricated product recommendation, and construction inspection.

Next, you learned about how to use the AI augmentation framework to find AI use cases in your current business problems, or those related to future goals, by using a strategic framework called SOAR. Then, you brainstormed various ideas and solutions with your team before prioritizing them based on their business viability and technical feasibility. Next, you learned how to bring your "quick-win" project to life in a prototype by ideating, building, and testing. You also learned how to test that prototype in pilot projects and scale it into your business to augment your capabilities and differentiate yourself in the market. By connecting your business strategy to the AI augmentation framework, you now know how to define an AI strategy that is in line with your business goals and expected outcomes.

In the final part of the book, you learned about three case studies that discussed AI in the real world – projects that are being developed and enhanced at the time of writing. The first was a project in conceptual design from Obayashi; the second looked at removing business-growth bottlenecks at ConXtech; and the third discussed welding inspections at Haskell. Importantly, each case study offered recommendations for others planning to implement an AI solution in their company.

Your AI journey won't stop after you go through the phases of the AI augmentation framework just once. You are always on that journey – a journey of invention, innovation, and exponential improvements. By the time you've been through all the phases once, your company will be more mature and at a different level from where you were when you started your AI journey: the AI use cases that might have been difficult now become easier to implement (remember the importance/difficulty matrix?). In other words, your "major strategic projects" become your "quick wins." So, keep going!

I wrote this book with your business in mind. That's why I included metrics about return on investment to make sure that you can grow your business over time. But I'd be shortsighted if I didn't mention that, at the end of the day, you are using AI to design and build better buildings and infrastructure for people – for us. I hope you find opportunities that empower your business ... *and* people ... *and* the planet.

As Hilda Espinal, the CTO of CannonDesign, explains:

"With AI we can exponentially grow the impact we can have on people's lives – people who use and occupy the spaces we design and build. At the end of the day it's all about people's lives, and this is the highest return on investment for using AI."

With this in mind, I want to take you back to the three wishes that I shared at the beginning of the book:

- First: I wish that this book helps you to identify AI use cases, develop tailored AI technologies, and define AI strategies that bring tremendous value to your company and our industry.
- Second: I wish that you can take the learning from this book to do something amazing for the good of other people and the planet.
- Third: I wish that you will share the learnings from your AI projects with the industry at large, to advance it as a whole and continue your AI journey.

The reason that I'm sharing these wishes again is that, without action, you'll achieve none of them. As an avid reader, I often read books, get lots of great ideas, take no action, and then forget what I learned. I don't want this to happen to you after reading this book.

It's time to put the learnings from this book into action.

To help you continue your AI journey, please go to www.aug-mentit-book.com and download the free workbook, which contains templates and activities to help you in your AI journey.

I hope you can use the information in this book, and the accompanying workbook, to make a big difference to our industry and the world. Together, we can.

Mehdi Nourbakhsh, PhD

CONNECT WITH ME

Thank you for reading this book. It means a lot to me.

I hope this book answered questions you might have had about AI strategy and its execution. I also hope that the framework proposed in this book can assist you in learning how to augment your business capabilities with AI.

I would love to hear what you liked about this book and how you are using it to create a better built environment for us and future generations. Don't hesitate to contact me and share how you are doing in your AI augmentation journey.

This book and the accompanying workbook will help you in your AI projects. If you need more resources, I have some offerings that you can find at www.augmentit-book.com:

- **Monthly readers' sessions (for a limited time only):** if you want to have a face-to-face conversation with me you can join my monthly readers' session, where other readers share how this book helped them create business value for their company.
- **AI workshop:** interested to discover the use case of AI in your business, or just want to learn more about AI? I offer a fully customized workshop program that can be run either in person or virtually. You can register as an individual or as a team to learn more about leveraging data and technologies to build a sustainable future tailored to your business.
- **AI course:** check out this course if you are interested in learning more about AI techniques and use cases created specifically for AEC executives, technologists, and innovation leaders. The

course aims to provide more details and examples from the AEC industry to help you fast-track your success.

- **YegaTech Consulting**: if you already have some ideas or have an AI use case prioritized, I'll be happy to bring your ideas to life and develop an AI technology for you. You can also book a consultation or a coaching session with me.

Contact or follow me for the latest updates and workshops or any questions you may have at:

🌐 mehdinourbakhsh.com
✉ Email: mehdi@mehdinour.com
in LinkedIn: https://www.linkedin.com/in/mehdinour/
🐦 Twitter: @MehdiNour_AEC

I look forward to working together and bringing tremendous value to your company, the industry, and the world.

Thank you!
Mehdi Nourbakhsh, PhD

ASKING FOR A FAVOR

Thanks again for reading *Augment It*. If you enjoyed reading this book, I'd be grateful if you would consider leaving an honest review on Amazon. As a first-time author, your feedback will help me to reach more readers, and potentially help other industry leaders like you. I believe that, together, we can change the AEC industry.

Happy reading,
Mehdi

REFERENCES

[1] K. International (2019). "Leaders and followers in the engineering & construction industry." *Global Construction Survey 2019*. https://assets. kpmg/content/dam/kpmg/xx/pdf/2016/09/global-construction-sur-vey-2016.pdf

[2] Verweij, G. and Rao, A. (2017). "Sizing the prize: What's the real value of AI for your business and how can you capitalise?" *PwC*. https:// www.pwc.com/gx/en/issues/analytics/assets/pwc-ai-analysis-sizing-the-prize-report.pdf

[3] Bughin, J., Seong, J., Manyika, J., Chui, M. and Joshi, R. (2018). "Notes from the AI frontier: Modeling the impact of AI on the world economy." *McKinsey*. https://www.mckinsey.com/featured-insights/artificial-intelligence/notes-from-the-ai-frontier-modeling-the-impact-of-ai-on-the-world-economy

[4] Ormerod, M. and Newton, R. (2013). "Construction as a career choice for young disabled people: Dispelling the myths," *Constr. Manag. Econ.*, vol. 31, no. 8, pp. 928–938. DOI: 10.1080/01446193.2013.777465

[5] Haupt, T. and Harinarain, N. (2017). "The image of the construction industry and its employment attractiveness." *Acta Structilia* 23(2). DOI: 10.18820/24150487/as23i2.4

[6] Ribeirinho, M. J. et al. (2020). "The next normal in construction." *McKinsey*. https://www.mckinsey.com/business-functions/operations/

our-insights/the-next-normal-in-construction-how-disruption-is-reshaping-the-worlds-largest-ecosystem

[7] McKinsey & Company (2017). "Reinventing construction: A route to higher productivity." *McKinsey*. http://www.mckinsey. com/industries/capital-projects-and-infrastructure/our-insights/ reinventing-construction-through-a-productivity-revolution

[8] Miksen, C. "Factors that affect the percentage of profit margins in construction." *Chron*. https://smallbusiness.chron.com/factors-af-fect-percentage-profit-margins-construction-35114.html, Access date: March 30, 2022.

[9] Barr, A. and Feigenbaum, E. A. (eds.) (1981). "Introduction." In *The Handbook of Artificial Intelligence* (pp. 1–17). Butterworth–Heinemann.

[10] Marcus, G. and Davis, E. (2019). *Rebooting AI: Building Artificial Intelligence We Can Trust*. Pantheon Books.

[11] Rittel, H. W. J. and Webber, M. M. (1973). "Dilemmas in a general theory of planning." *Policy Science 4*(2). DOI: 10.1007/BF01405730.

[12] Olson, P. (2016, March 10). "Google's A.I. program AlphaGo claims second victory against 'Go' champion." *Forbes*. https://www.forbes.com/sites/parmyolson/2016/03/10/ google-alphago-second-win-go-champion/?sh=7351705b7bf8

[13] SAE International (2021, April 30). "Taxonomy and definitions for terms related to driving automation systems for on-road motor vehicles." *SAE International*. https://www.sae.org/standards/content/j3016_202104

[14] Dennett, D. (1986). "Cognitive wheels: The frame problem of AI."

In Hookway, C. (ed.), *Minds, Machines, and Evolution: Philosophical Studies* (pp. 129–152). Cambridge University Press.

[15] Pearl, J. and Mackenzie, D. (2018). *The Book of Why: The New Science of Cause and Effect*, Chapter 10, pp. 349, Kindle Edition, Basic books.

[16] Gandel, S. (2021, November 2). "Zillow, facing big losses, quits flipping houses and will lay off a quarter of its staff." *The New York Times*. https://www.nytimes.com/2021/11/02/business/zillow-q3-earnings-home-flipping-ibuying.html

[17] Dastin, J. (2018, October 10). "Amazon scraps secret AI recruiting tool that showed bias against women." *Reuters*. https://www.reuters.com/article/us-amazon-com-jobs-automation-insight-idUSKCN1MK08G

[18] Javanbakht, A. and Saab, L. (2017, October 26). "The science of fright: Why we love to be scared." *The Conversation*. https://theconversation.com/the-science-of-fright-why-we-love-to-be-scared-85885

[19] Watkins, M. (2007, September 10). "Demystifying strategy: The what, who, how, and why." *Harvard Business Review*. https://hbr.org/2007/09/demystifying-strategy-the-what

[20] Stavros, J. M. and Hinrichs, G. (2021). *Learning to SOAR: Creating Strategy that Inspires Innovation and Engagement*. SOAR Institute.

[21] GroupMap (2022). "SOAR analysis template." https://www.groupmap.com/map-templates/soar-analysis/

[22] Cukier, Kenneth, Viktor Mayer-Schönberger, and Francis de Véricourt. *Framers: Human advantage in an age of technology and turmoil*. Penguin, 2021.

ACKNOWLEDGMENTS

When I started this book project, I did not know what I was getting myself into. I used to remind myself that I wrote my PhD dissertation in one year while working for Autodesk during the day, and I thought that writing a book surely couldn't be more difficult than that. But I was wrong!

Writing this book has been a journey to discover myself. It took me down memory lane to places that I had forgotten. It took me to people who shaped my life and helped me grow. Without them, I had nothing to write about.

I want to say a big THANK YOU to all of you beautiful people who were part of my authorship journey.

Let me start at the end.

Firstly, I'd like to thank my talented, fantastic, and fabulous book coach Kelly Irving, the mastermind behind this book. She was with me through every step of the authorship journey, and found me when I was lost in the darkness of my mind. With her mindful questions, she shed light that gave me clarity on what to say and how to say it. I cannot recommend her more!

Second, I'd like to thank Scott A. MacMillan, my brilliant editor Carolyn Jackson, and the design and production team at Grammar Factory, who made my first publishing experience pleasing.

Third, I am very appreciative of my beta readers, who read the manuscript and provided feedback on how to improve it. Without your help and support, I could not have improved this book as much as I did. In this category, my special thanks go to Dr. John Haymaker for reading the raw and unedited version of the manuscript and providing early feedback on the overall direction of the book. Thank you as well to Derek Cunz (Mortenson), Devin Gray (VIATechnik), Will Scarbrough (VHB), Alain Waha (Buro Happold), Benjamin Callam (McCarthy), Eric Law (Swinerton), Hamzah Shanbari (Haskell), James Detzel (Austin Commercial), Jit Kee Chin (Suffolk), Niels W. Falk (HD Lab), Shane Burger (Woods Bagot), Yoshito Tsuji (Obayashi), Dace Campbell (McKinstry), Mark Wartenberg (Nike), Yehia Madkour (Perkins & Will), Jim Stoddart (Autodesk), Chin-Yi Cheng (Autodesk), Anand Rajagopal (Autodesk), Victor Okhoya (Perkins & Will), and Andrew Starr (Gensler).

Fourth, I am grateful to all the thought leaders interviewed in the book, who shared their projects with me and recommended how I could make this book beneficial to our industry: Alain Waha (Buro Happold), Benjamin Callam (McCarthy), Derek Cunz (Mortenson), Eric Law (Swinerton), Gilles Caussade (ConXtech), Hamzah Shanbari (Haskell), Hilda Espinal (CannonDesign), James Detzel (Austin Commercial), Jit Kee Chin (Suffolk), John Haymaker (Perkins & Will), Nick Bagatelos (BAGS), Niels W. Falk (HD Lab), Paul Murphy (GHD), Scott Peters (Construction Robotics), Shane Burger (Woods Bagot), Tessa Lau (Dusty Robotics), and Yoshito Tsuji (Obayashi).

Fifth, I'd like to thank all the AEC professionals who spent their time with me to share their expertise, knowledge, and advice: Andrew Starr (Gensler), Calvin Kam (SBI International), Dace Campbell (McKinstry), Ernesto M. Aieta (MWH Constructors), Lin Wu (OgwaFacade), Mark Wartenberg (Nike), Min Song (SBI International), Reece Poth (Guardian Industries), Sabrina Odah (Suffolk), Saurabh Gangwar (CODA), Tony Rinella (SBI International), Tyler Convery (DeSimone), and Yehia Madkour (Perkins & Will).

Sixth, I'd like to thank all my managers and former colleagues at Autodesk. I grew, learned, and became the technologist I am today with your help and guidance. Thanks to Mike Haley, Mark Davis, Gonzalo Martinez, David Benjamin, Erin Bradner, Anthony Ruto, Rick Rundell, Michael Bergin, Yi Wang, Kai-hung Chang, Chin-Yi Cheng, Dianne

Gault, Clayton Hotson, John Schmier, Tim Towles, and the entire AEC Industry Futures team. You rock!

Seventh, I'd like to thank my university professors and academic heroes who helped me see the science behind the AEC industry and computer science: Dr. Javier Irizarry, who helped me navigate my PhD study with his kindness; Prof. Chuck Eastman, my late academic father, who taught me leadership, critical thinking, and perseverance; and Dr. Rosli Mohamad Zin, who introduced me to research.

Eighth, I'd like to thank my parents and family, who taught me to never give up. My special thanks go to my beautiful and brilliant partner in work and life, Samaneh, who was my best mentor, advisor, and cheerleader. Her name, without a doubt, should have been on the cover of this book. I doubt I would have gotten this far without your support, so thank you. I love you.

Last, I'd like to thank you, my dearest reader, who wants to change the AEC industry for the good of the people and the planet. Thank you for who you are, and I cheer you on your journey to greatness.

Mehdi Nourbakhsh

Printed in the USA
CPSIA information can be obtained
at www.ICGtesting.com
LVHW091328021123
762340LV00004B/155